"You Don't Need Stan Anymore. Now That You Have Me . . ."

"What do you mean, 'now that I have you'?" she whispered hoarsely. "I don't have you. I don't even want you. . . ."

"Don't you, Perris?" His hand was moving along the bare skin between her shoulder blades, then up again to cradle the back of her head. "Can't you feel how good we're going to be together?" he asked huskily. "Can't you feel the spell beginning?"

She did feel it. She'd felt it from the first. But she knew it spelled disaster for her. She knew she must fight against it with all her strength.

RAYE MORGAN

lives in California, where she was born, although she spent parts of her childhood in both Holland and Guam. She has always wanted to write, a dream her geologist husband and four young sons are happy to support.

Dear Reader:

SILHOUETTE DESIRE is an exciting new line of contemporary romances from Silhouette Books. During the past year, many Silhouette readers have written in telling us what other types of stories they'd like to read from Silhouette, and we've kept these comments and suggestions in mind in developing SILHOUETTE DESIRE.

DESIREs feature all of the elements you like to see in a romance, plus a more sensual, provocative story. So if you want to experience all the excitement, passion and joy of falling in love, then SILHOUETTE DESIRE is for you.

I hope you enjoy this book and all the wonderful stories to come from SILHOUETTE DESIRE. I'd appreciate any thoughts you'd like to share with us on new SILHOUETTE DESIRE, and I invite you to write to us at the address below:

> Karen Solem
> Editor-in-Chief
> Silhouette Books
> P.O. Box 769
> New York, N.Y. 10019

RAYE MORGAN
Summer Wind

Silhouette Desire

Published by Silhouette Books New York

America's Publisher of Contemporary Romance

Other Silhouette Books by Raye Morgan

Embers of the Sun

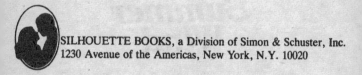

SILHOUETTE BOOKS, a Division of Simon & Schuster, Inc.
1230 Avenue of the Americas, New York, N.Y. 10020

ISBN: 0-671-47498-7

First Silhouette Books printing November, 1983

10 9 8 7 6 5 4 3 2 1

America's Publisher of Contemporary Romance

Printed in the U.S.A.

BC91

Summer Wind

1

~~~~~~~~~~~~~~~~

The first thing she noticed was his eyes. As she rolled back on her fluffy beach towel, shading her face against the shimmering sun, trying to see whose careless step had kicked a spray of golden sand across her bare legs, his brilliant eyes seemed bluer than the azure desert sky behind him.

His grin was wide and without a hint of apology. She could see that given half a chance, he would take her stare as an opening, so she frowned, putting up an immediate barrier, and he walked on.

She lay her head back down on her arms, but her coffee-colored gaze followed the man as he headed down the shore line. Absently, she admired his tan, muscular body. With his shaggy thatch of sun-bleached blond hair, he looked like a Polynesian prince walking toward the sea. His shoulders gleamed in the sunlight, emphasizing their width, and she noted that he moved with the elegant grace of an athlete.

Nice, she thought to herself. In fact, very, very nice.

Grinning to herself, she stopped her thoughts. No more of that, Perris, my girl, she mused. Now that you're happily engaged, it's time to bow out of that sort of game. After all, what would Stan say?

Perris Fleming stretched her slender, well-shaped body and thought about Stan. What a darling he'd been to wait for her so long. He had wanted to marry her the moment she'd graduated from college, but she'd put him off. She'd had her dream to follow.

Grimacing, she closed her eyes and hid her face from the relentless desert sun. Her dream. It was hard to believe that it was all over, that she would never play concert violin. But reality had to be faced at some point. After three years of intense study, it was surely time for her to face the truth. She just wasn't good enough.

The three years in Vienna had flown by. She felt like a woman of the world now. After all, she was twenty-five; she'd seen Europe, traveled through the Orient and driven across the United States by herself. She'd had her pocket picked in Paris, been propositioned in Soho and had a brief but very tempestuous romance with an artist in a garret in Vienna. She'd had her fling. It was time to settle down.

Very soon, Perris Fleming was to metamorphose into Mrs. Stanley Fremont. Her life was set. She had no time to waste on handsome strangers on the beach.

She raised her head, propping up her chin on her cupped hands, looking to see what the man was doing now. He seemed to be wrestling something out of the water, and as she watched, she realized that it was a sailboard. After he'd carefully packed it away in his canvas carrier, he stood still, legs apart, gazing at the sailboats gliding by a few hundred yards out, their sails a play of red, yellow and white against the intensely blue water.

Now that she thought about it, what was he doing there? Although the beach wasn't exactly private, it fronted a very exclusive group of condominiums, and everyone assumed that the shore line went with the property. The residents had little trouble with tourists and had almost grown to view the entire crescent as their own.

The beach was a pleasant strip of coarse sand, separated from a parking lot by a fence that supported a thick hedge of oleanders, covered with white blossoms under the hot desert sun. A small wooden footbridge spanned the drainage ditch that paralleled the fence, so that the beach seemed to be almost an island, set apart.

The same people went there year after year. Perris's family had bought their condo when she was ten, and she'd spent every summer and many a spring vacation at Lake Havasu ever since. She knew every resident of Havapai Shore, at least by sight. And she'd never seen this man before.

Why hadn't she thought to ask him what he was doing there when he was walking by? It was obvious that he didn't belong. Whereas any other summer visitor would be wearing fashionable walking shorts, he was dressed in faded cutoff jeans. Instead of being carefully styled, his hair was badly in need of a trim. And most telling of all, he had too dark a tan.

Perris and all her friends were still very pale from a long winter huddled in graduate-school classrooms or in skyscraper office buildings. Even in Los Angeles there wasn't much tanning to be done during the usually overcast, gloomy spring days, so no one had developed that pleasing shade of almond brown they all hungered for. They were still the color of fresh ivory. Either that or a bright lobster red from too much sun too fast.

But a tan such as this man had could only be

developed over long, nurturing hours in the sun. He'd been out here for months.

From this distance, Perris would judge his age to be in the thirties. What could he possibly have been doing here all that time? Didn't he have a job to go to?

The beach was deserted. Perris was the only resident who'd ventured out that day. She half thought that perhaps she ought to go out on the pier and ask him his business, but then she let that idea slip away. She was too lazy, too satisfied lying there in the sun.

As she stared at the man, his image began to fade, and she found herself enjoying the larger picture. The lake was so incredibly lovely. Set at the eastern border of the deadly Mojave Desert, Lake Havasu glistened like a blue piece of sky that had been torn out and flung down onto the hot, golden sand.

The landscape all around the lake had its own special beauty. Stark and eerie as a moonscape, though painted brown and golden rather than black and white, it was wild, untamed and very dangerous.

But there, beside the lake, that was forgotten. There the land was safe, the water was abundant and Perris felt at home.

The sun was warm on her shoulders; the sand beneath her, comfortably soft. She snuggled down onto her bright orange towel, enjoying the silky feel of her dark auburn hair as it lay heavily on her naked back, then slipped slowly down across her shoulders until it spread in flaming ribbons to cradle her head. In moments, she was asleep.

The first thought that came to her when she woke up was that it was time to get out of the sun. Even before she sat up, she could feel the tight, crisp sensation on her back where the tiny, spaghetti-thin strap touched. She knew she'd burned.

Groaning, she raised herself cross-legged on her towel and looked about her. A sudden sound from behind revealed what had awakened her.

Turning, she found herself staring into a dozen pairs of laughing male eyes. Each impudent pair was attached to a gangly teenaged body, and the whole motley crew was standing on the bridge that she would have to use to get off the beach and back home.

Rotten luck, she thought ruefully. Jeffrey Newman must have brought his entire prep school water polo team out for the weekend.

Perris wasn't shy, but she was somewhat daunted by the prospect of making her way, in her skimpiest bikini, through a crowd of leering boys who were barely beyond adolescence. Already low whistles and murmured smart remarks were floating her way through the afternoon air.

But she had to get off the beach, or she'd soon be burned beyond recognition. Resolutely, she rose and folded her towel, slipped into her thongs, then began the march toward the bridge.

Just a few steps away from it, she faltered, stopping to glare at the boys. They seemed to be preparing for something. Were they going to let her through? They had the look of gate keepers, set to demand a forfeit for granting her the right to pass. Suddenly, visions of being lost forever among them, never to find her way back out into the postpubescent world, struck her with a sharp apprehension. Wasn't there some other way to get off this beach?

"It's okay."

Involved in her own problems, Perris had forgotten all about the stranger. But now he'd come up behind her and was taking her arm.

"Don't give it another thought," he said softly, his

blue eyes glinting with a warm light. "I'll help you run the gauntlet."

She frowned, a bit bewildered.

"We'll just pretend we're lovers." His smile crinkled the corners of his eyes. She noticed how blond his eyelashes were, nearly white at the tips, then almost red back near the eyelids. "Come on. You can pretend, can't you?"

She nodded slowly, and he put his arm carefully around her burned shoulders. Suddenly, she was very aware of how much bare flesh his arm was in contact with, but she bit her lip and steeled herself. He pulled her close against him, and they walked up to the bridge.

"Good afternoon, men," he said cheerfully as they made their way past the disappointed boys. "Great day for a swim."

Perris could see remarks trembling on callow lips, but as each young man looked into the face of her protector, he seemed to feel that silence was the better choice. As they reached the far side of the bridge, there were even some muttered Have a nice days, and Perris caught sight of Jeffrey Newman, who smiled sheepishly.

"Thank you," she murmured as they found themselves in the dark-asphalt parking lot.

"Don't thank me," he retorted softly, still holding her. "I enjoyed it."

She glanced up at his incredibly blue eyes. "You can let me go now," she said pointedly. "We're over the bridge."

"Do I have to?" His fingers moved on her shoulder, his arm holding her in its friendly curve. "You seem to fit so well."

She began to wonder how she was going to disentangle herself without an embarrassing struggle. Had she traded in a minor irritation for a major problem? But then he released her, letting his fingertips glide across her back as he did so, creating a trail of tiny goose bumps.

"I enjoyed it," he said again. "It isn't every day I get to rescue a beautiful maiden in distress."

"I wasn't really in distress," she protested, frowning at him. Instinctively, she felt that she should maintain a position of strength with this man. He had the look of a wolf who, sensing weakness, would feel no hesitation at moving in for the kill. He couldn't be that much older than she was—perhaps six or seven years. But he had an air of calm maturity, of knowing what he wanted and having no hesitation in asserting his demands, that left her a bit uneasy. "I could have made it alone if I'd had to."

"Could you?" His smile showed that he thought differently. "I guess we'll never know."

She should be going. For some reason, this man made her feel awkward in a way that was new to her. She wanted to leave him quickly, but she couldn't force herself on. Something in his eyes held her there.

"Well, thank you again." Nothing else came to mind, so she stuck her hand out. "I'm Perris Fleming," she said quickly as his huge hand enveloped her slender one. "I live in the condominium on the far corner."

"Robert Chase," he answered, but his failure to offer an address was loud and clear.

He let her hand go as though he were reluctant to, and his sparkling eyes began a slow examination of her overexposed body. Nervously, she held her folded towel up in front of herself, wishing as she did so that she could open it and drape it around her shoulders. But to do that would be to let him know just how shy she was before his gaze, and she wanted to keep that from him if at all possible.

"I haven't seen you here before," she said.

"I haven't been here before," he answered.

"Did you buy someone's condo?" Somehow she had to prompt him into telling her where he was staying. "Or are you visiting someone in the area?"

"Neither."

Neither? The next question, Then what are you doing loitering in this neighborhood? trembled on the tip of her tongue, but she just couldn't quite say it.

He was so awfully attractive. His straw-blond hair shaded his face so that his sparkling blue eyes seemed to burn even brighter. His features had a rugged strength, a sort of Viking arrogance, and he was so tall that her eyebrows came only to the middle of his chest.

As she gazed speculatively at him, he stood easily before her, his eyes shimmering with an awareness of her thoughts.

"I noticed you have a sailboard," she probed tentatively.

He nodded. "Have you tried wind surfing?" he asked.

"No." She hadn't meant to be quite so emphatic, but perhaps it was best, after all. He'd noticed and cocked one eyebrow inquiringly.

"You're not a sailor?" he asked. "And living in this perfect spot?" It was as though she'd admitted an allergy to water.

"I take it you are," she said instead of answering directly.

His affirmative response lit his blue eyes with a silver glow. "The sailing has been great," he told her. "It's been nice and quiet around here." He grimaced. "Until this weekend, anyway. All of a sudden, the place is swarming with summer visitors."

She smiled back. "That's the way it always is. I haven't been here much lately. I've been out of the country for the last few years and only had a few days here each summer. But I can remember how it was." Her grin was impish. "Just wait," she warned. "It'll get worse."

"Too bad." A faraway look glazed his eyes, and he turned to gaze out at the glistening water of the lake. She had the sudden thought that he saw a dream there, a shining goal very like her own. But when he looked at her again, all she saw in his eyes was the male response that seemed so close to the surface with him.

"Well," she added a bit stiffly, "I'm sorry if we vacationers are getting in your way."

"Oh, no." He grinned. "You're the nicest thing to clutter up my path in a long time. I knew from the moment I saw you lying on my beach that fate was stepping in."

Fate? What on earth was he talking about? A bit confused, she ignored that and zeroed in on his use of the possessive. " 'Your beach'?" she asked sardonically. "Have you made a recent purchase?"

She expected a nonchalant grin and was surprised to see the faraway look again instead.

"No," he answered slowly. "But I'd grown to think of it as my own lately. No one else seemed to use it." Then came the grin. "Until you showed up today."

She felt a twinge of resentment at the way he was looking her over again. His azure eyes were skimming along the length of her bare legs, from the spot on one rounded hip where the tiny orange tie held the bottom of her suit together, down across the defenseless flesh, to her sandaled feet with their apricot-painted toenails. There was something a shade too familiar about the way he was looking at her. Pointedly, she cleared her throat to recapture his attention.

His smile would have been disarming in any situation.

"Sorry," he said brightly. "I get carried away when I

come in contact with beautiful objects. A painting, a sculpture, a lovely"—he glanced down at her again—"leg. It's all the same. I can't seem to control it."

He was laughing at her. Perris lifted her chin and tried to glare. She was determined to show no weakness. "As long as you look but don't touch," she advised.

His blue eyes opened wide in mock distress. "But touching is a part of it all," he informed her earnestly.

Suddenly, she found him moving close again, and she seemed unable to avoid him. His darkly tanned hand was on her shoulder, gently lifting the strap to the top of her swimming suit so he could slide his fingers beneath it.

"If I couldn't touch you," he said huskily as she gazed up at him in disbelief, "I wouldn't know that your skin is smoother than the inner curl of a tropic wave, warmer than an August night, more seductive than a siren's song. Would I?"

While he spoke, his fingers were moving slowly across her shoulder, pulling away the strap so that her top gaped open, revealing a generous portion of alabaster breast. Perris felt stunned, confused. Her sensual defenses had never been attacked in quite such a manner before, and her bewildered mind was having trouble taking in just what was going on.

By the time she realized that it was something she had to stop, he was so close that she was sure he was about to kiss her. She put both hands on his naked chest to push him away, then recoiled from the sensation of her fingers sliding through the roughness of his golden chest hair.

"Stop it!" The words flew from her lips, and suddenly, as though someone had waved a magic wand, the mood was totally different.

"You do have quite a burn, you know," he said, holding up her strap indifferently as he inspected her skin in much the way a brother or a doctor might. "You'd better get something on that quickly. My mother used to swear by a rubdown with cold tea." He shook his head semiseriously. "Use whatever you like, but get something working soon."

She stared at him. Had it been her imagination? Was the sun affecting her brain? She'd been so sure that they'd been in the midst of a wild and sensual interlude. Now, suddenly, it was nothing of the sort. Was she mad? Or was he very clever?

"I will," she answered lamely.

"For all your dark eyes, your skin is very light, isn't it?"

She nodded, watching him from behind thickly clustered lashes. Why didn't she turn on her heel and walk off? What was it that was keeping her there? She wasn't sure she really wanted to know the answer to that.

"I do burn easily," she responded slowly.

His eyes were full of some deeper knowledge as he nodded his understanding. "I can see that you do."

His voice was so soft that she tilted her head as though struggling to hear his words.

He put out one finger and ran it gently along her collarbone. "We'll have to make sure you stay out of danger."

His eyes were laughing again. She pulled away from his touch, but she wasn't really offended. In fact, the whole scene was beginning to strike her as rather funny.

This attractive man, this Robert Chase, had taken liberties no stranger should have dared. And yet he didn't frighten her. In fact, now that the shock had dulled, she began to think she rather liked him. Maybe even a little too much. Enough, anyway, to give him a bit of his own back.

"*Your* tan is gorgeous," she offered, looking him over with a purposefully belligerent air, forcing back the laughter that rose in her throat. Let him see what it felt like to be judged like a piece of livestock. "You must have spent months on it."

"You like it, do you?" He looked down, flexing his shoulders as he did so, as though surprised and curious himself as to how dark he'd become. "Actually, I managed to get all that in the last month or so. I tan pretty quickly."

"For a blond," she murmured, noting his shaggy flaxen hair.

He grinned, reaching up and running a dark hand through his mane. "Do you doubt the authenticity?" he asked, amused. "Want to check my roots?"

She shook her head, trying to hold back her own sudden grin. "Of course not. I didn't mean that. It's just . . . unusual for a blond to tan so darkly."

His grin was wide and suggestive. "I'm an unusual sort of guy. You'll come to realize that once we get to know each other better."

Getting to know Robert Chase better would be exciting. A tingle spread across her skin at the thought of it, for there was a measure of sensuality to this man that was truly entrancing. But what was the matter with her? There would be no getting to know him better. Reality came rushing back. "Oh . . ." She began to back away, shaking her head. "I'm . . ." Somehow she couldn't just come right out and say she was engaged.

But his hand was on her upper arm, stopping her retreat.

"You're what?" he said softly. Then his eyes lit up with a wicked fire. "You're not used to unusual men, are you, Perris?"

He was laughing at her again. Her temper flared, as it so often did. "I'm not used to being grabbed by strangers, if that's what you mean," she shot out, pulling against his grip, but to no avail.

"We're not strangers." His voice was low, almost like the purr of a large jungle cat. "We've introduced ourselves, and I've saved you from the dragons"—he glanced back at the boys, who were still roughhousing on the bridge—"or dragonlings, or whatever." His smile warmed her again. "I'd say we're even more than friends by now. Closer to something much more intimate."

Perris felt a tremor of alarm. He was an unusual man, at least in the scope of her experience. What did she know of him, after all? What did she know of his background, his family? What was she doing standing there talking like this to a perfect stranger?

Robert Chase was not the sort of man she was used to at all. His shaggy appearance indicated a meager income. He was in an exclusive neighborhood, but he didn't look as though he belonged there. And his manner was like nothing she'd ever encountered before.

For all she knew, he might be some sort of weirdo. She knew it was time to extricate herself from this situation and make tracks for home.

"You're hurting my sunburn," she said firmly. "Please let me go."

His fingers released her immediately. "I'm sorry." His sincere regret made her feel just a tiny bit guilty, because the sunburn had not yet begun to sting at all. But still, she was free.

"Where are you staying?" she asked as she backed away.

He cocked a thick eyebrow. "Planning to visit me?" he asked hopefully.

"No, I'm just curious." She was out of danger now. If he wanted to do anything more, he would have to make a running start, and she'd always been pretty swift on her feet.

"Curiosity can lead to danger," he called to her as she moved farther away from where he was standing. "And frustrated curiosity can motivate interesting behavior."

She took that to mean that he wasn't going to tell her, but instead of feeling annoyed, she found herself laughing. "Have it your way," she called back, swinging into her usual energetic walk. "See you around."

"You can count on it," he answered.

She kept going, knowing that he was watching her but afraid to give him the wrong idea by looking back.

The wrong idea. What was the right idea? He fascinated her. She still felt high with the excitement he had created. But that was ridiculous. It was the spirit of the encounter that had charmed her, not the man. Wasn't it?

2

Fascination was a fleeting thing. As she turned into her yard, she risked a look back. He was gone.

"And now, Perris, my girl," she told herself sternly as she opened one of the huge double doors that led into her foyer, "you will suspend fascination and forget that you ever saw that man. Immediately!"

"Perris? Is that you?"

Her mother's voice was thin and weak, but it made its way down to Perris before she even began the climb up to the second floor where the living area was situated.

"Yes, Mother," she answered. She felt the usual twinge of guilt at the delicate sound of her mother's voice. "Here I am, in the flesh."

The older woman lay back on an ivory-colored, linen-covered couch. The sheer inner drapes that fell from the ceiling to cover one entire side of the room were drawn so that the light was muted, emphasizing the subtle, dusky quality of the decorating.

The walls were antique white, the carpeting the faded shade of red roses pressed between books in Victorian day rooms, the various upholstered chairs either a pale mauve or the color of desert hills in the late-evening light.

"In the flesh indeed," Mrs. Fleming admonished softly, gazing in wonder at the lightly clad body before her. "I don't know why you insist on wandering the streets naked like you do."

Perris laughed as she leaned forward to drop a light kiss on her mother's soft cheek. "It's my Lady Godiva complex, Mother," she teased. "All I need is a white horse."

"Heaven forbid." Her mother surveyed her critically. "You certainly are a woman now, aren't you?" she said with bemusement.

Perris laughed. "I've been a woman for years and years. You just haven't been paying attention."

Mrs. Fleming tried a slight smile. "Oh, I've known it," she answered softly. "I sometimes wondered if you did." Her smile broadened. "But now you're finally ready to step out and meet your future. I'm so glad . . . so happy. . . ." The last was uttered weakly, and she leaned back against the couch again, as though wearied by the conversation.

Perris frowned. "Can I get you anything?" she asked anxiously, regretting that she'd stayed away so long.

Mrs. Fleming's carefully painted lips curved in a tiny smile, but she shook her head. "I'm fine, dear, now that you're here."

Perris cursed herself once again for her thoughtlessness. While she'd been lured into sparring with the stranger on the beach, her mother had been waiting there, alone and lonely. She mustn't let it happen again.

Her mother hadn't always been this way, so weak, so dependent, and Perris was sure this phase wouldn't last much longer. But until her mother felt well enough to take on the world again, Perris had made it her own responsibility to be everything that her mother could want.

Her father's death had been sudden, an unexpected heart attack that had struck while he was playing golf. After a life of living only for her husband and her marriage, Mrs. Fleming had been stunned, unable to cope, unable to find a new direction for her days. Her only consolation had been Perris's arrival at their home in Beverly Hills a few weeks earlier.

The shrill sound of the telephone ripped through the room.

"That will be Stanley," Mrs. Fleming said with some satisfaction as Perris went to pick up the receiver. "He's been calling every ten minutes for the last hour."

Stan's voice was slightly indignant as he answered her greeting. "Where have you been all afternoon?" he demanded.

Perris smiled in spite of herself. She could picture the worried frown between his feathered dark brows, the long fingers tapping on the oak desk in the study of the Fremont home. She knew him as well as she knew anyone in the world.

"I ran down to the beach for a bit of sunbathing," she told him lightly. "And what have you been up to?"

He sighed. "Missing you, mainly. I've seen so little of you since you got back from Vienna."

She swept the thick hair back from her neck, letting the cool, air-conditioned breeze flow over her skin as she leaned against the arm that held the phone. "That's what this summer will be all about," she reminded him. "That's why you took a leave of absence from your father's business and I took these two months off. We're going to get to know each other all over again, so that we're sure, before the wedding."

His growl was impatient. "I've told you a hundred times that I don't need that. I'm already sure. I've been sure since we were both in junior high. It's been you who's felt the need to run out into the world and 'find yourself.' I've never been lost."

Perris grinned into the receiver. Good old Stan. He had a faith that never wavered.

No, he'd never been lost. And he never would be. From childhood on, he'd had a clear idea of what he wanted from life. Perris only wished she'd been blessed with such certainty.

"I'm insisting upon this for both our sakes, Stan, and you know it," she admonished.

He sniffed, but seemed ready to drop the subject. "What about tonight?" he asked, shifting gears. "A bunch of the old gang are in town. They're meeting at Jocko's, just like in the old days. Want to go along?"

Perris bit her lip. "Oh, Stan, I'm not sure I should. I left Mother alone all afternoon and—"

"I've already spoken to her about it, and she gave her blessing."

Perris shook her head ruefully. Stan was the son of Mrs. Fleming's best friend, Ruth Fremont. The two of them had planned that their children would marry from the beginning, and now that it finally seemed about to come to pass, both were delighted.

Stan had always been a particular favorite with her mother. His tall, dark good looks and courtly manner won her over every time. He could wrap her around his finger with a smile. If Stan had already asked, Perris knew she might as well make plans to go.

She arranged a suitable time with Stan, then hung up the receiver and turned back to where her mother was waiting.

"It *was* Stan, wasn't it?" Her mother's huge brown

eyes glowed with pleasure. "I can't tell you how happy I am that you and he are finally getting married."

Perris slipped down beside her mother on the couch. "I know it, Mom." She smiled as she took the older woman's hand in her own. "And you know how happy it makes me to make you happy."

They both laughed at the silly statement, and Perris squeezed the blue-veined hand she held. She felt her own eyes brimming with tears and quickly looked away.

It touched her to see her mother smile. That expression was so seldom on her face these days. Perris could remember when it had been different, when her mother's good humor had kept the family sane and safe through any crisis.

Her father had been a large, quiet man, prone to dark moods and reflective silences. Her mother had complemented her father like a butterfly might complement a reluctant turtle, teasing him out of his shell with a few flashy swoops of her wings, soothing him with a feathery kiss, delighting them all with her acrobatics.

But now the butterfly's wings were stilled. There was no one to flutter for. Perris prayed that she might help bring the life back into her mother's eyes and see her dance in the sun again soon.

"I don't like to leave you," she told her now. "Just say the word and I'll stay. We could play cards, watch a little TV—"

"Oh, no, darling." Her mother seemed appalled at the idea. "Don't you know what a thrill it is for me to see you with Stanley?" She leaned her silver curls back against the couch, her eyes misted with dreams. "It reminds me of the way your father and I were. The fun we had together. When the two of you marry, it will be just like watching myself going through it all over again."

Perris looked away, suddenly uncomfortable. Stanley wasn't a bit like her father, and Perris was hardly like her mother, either. She was a little afraid of the dependency her mother was displaying. But this dwelling on the past couldn't go on much longer, she assured herself. After all, her mother was still deep in mourning. Soon she would come out into the light again.

Suddenly, a picture of Robert Chase, the handsome stranger on the beach, flashed into her mind. There had been laughter in his eyes and warmth in his smile. Perris had the fleeting wish that somehow that joy in life could be channeled into helping her mother. But that was a foolish fancy. Her mother would hardly look kindly on someone of Robert's type. And he didn't seem like the sort who would want to spend his days cheering up a lonely widow.

She pushed the thought away and rose to fix her mother a light meal on a tray.

"Nothing for me, darling," her mother protested once she realized what her daughter was doing. "I couldn't eat a thing."

But Perris made her a quick salad, anyway: butter lettuce and asparagus stalks studded with fat, pink shrimp. She tossed it in a blue porcelain bowl and set a tall glass of ice tea alongside on a yellow linen mat before she presented the meal, trying to make it look as appetizing as possible.

Then she retreated to her room at the back of the house to prepare for her date with Stan.

Her bedroom at home in Beverly Hills was furnished lavishly and filled with mementos of classes taken and football games cheered for, of jobs tried and lessons learned.

But this was her vacation room. In it there was nothing to remind her of school or work. This room was furnished in Danish modern. The walls were covered with posters from beach and ski resorts. The bookcase was filled with fat novels that had helped fill many a long summer afternoon, and the closet was stuffed with sports clothes.

Her huge picture window looked out over the emerald green of a landscaped area set between the rows of condominiums. In the distance lay the dark, brooding volcanic mountains. And over all gleamed the stunning blue desert sky.

Perris stared out at the landscape, then whirled and pulled something from her closet. It was the black case that held her violin, the Guarneri that had been so much a part of her for the last three years.

Reverently, she opened it and let her forefinger slide slowly down the A string, listening to the tiny buzzing sound it made. Then she plucked the instrument quickly from its case and placed the padded rest under her chin, holding the bow ready, as though about to sweep into a flaming passage from a favorite concerto.

Closing her eyes, she stood there motionless. She could hear the music in her head, but she didn't dare let it fill the air. Her bow never touched the strings, and finally, she lowered them both, tucked them away again and prepared for her bath.

As the silvery water cascaded over her freshly burned shoulders, she reached to turn down the hot water quickly until it reached a temperature that didn't bring out the sting. Then she closed her eyes again, letting the water flow around her, still hearing the music.

The music would always be there. She knew that. Even though she'd now turned her back on it, the strains of its seduction followed her everywhere.

She'd always been a very talented musician. Her parents had been pleased at first, proud when she won local competitions. But when she had told them that she planned to make music her career, they had been aghast.

"What kind of a life is that?" her father had stormed. "Playing for pennies in the park? Traveling like a gypsy from town to town? Giving lessons to sniveling children?"

Much better that she should marry Stanley and become an executive's wife. That was a role they all understood.

She'd fought them. Her three years in Vienna had received only grudging acceptance from her family. And when she'd finally been forced to accept her limitations, to face the fact that she'd never be among the very greatest in the world, she'd agreed to come home and live the life they'd always wanted for her.

What a shame that her father had died before her return. It still saddened her to think of how happy she could have made him if she'd only done it a year earlier. She should have been with her mother when the crisis came. She felt strongly that she had failed her parents when they needed her most.

But she would do her best to make that up to her mother. From now on, Perris would be happy in the way her mother wanted for her, not grasping for something just out of reach.

She put on a light, pumpkin-colored cotton gauze dress. The skirt was smocked at the hip, then flared out in a circle that left the fabric hugging her long legs as she walked. The top slipped down off the shoulders, peasant style, exposing the fresh new attempt she'd made at a tan.

She wore her dark red hair swinging loosely about her neck and attached large gold crescents to her ears. Then she ran down the stairs to open the double doors to Stan at the sound of the doorbell.

His eyes widened appreciatively at the sight of her. "Wow," he said, "you look like a flame in that thing."

A flame. That was what she felt like. There was something burning within her, some excitement, some anticipation.

"Shall we go?" she asked, but he was shaking his head.

"Just let me run up and say hi to your mother," he answered, and she smiled, liking him for that.

It was almost ten minutes before they walked out to the sidewalk. Stan held open the door of his shiny silver Mercedes, and Perris dropped into the passenger seat. As Stan started the engine and began to move the car out into the street, Perris looked up and met a pair of sparkling blue eyes smiling at her from across the way. She barely had time to register Robert's identity before the car she was in had turned the corner, leaving him behind.

For some reason, the blood was pounding in her veins. That one glimpse had set off a storm in her system. She gripped her hands together tightly in her lap, trying to fight back the wild feeling that swirled within.

It was nothing. She'd merely caught a quick glimpse of a man she'd met on the beach. What was the matter with her?

But what had he been doing there? Was he watching her house?

No, now she was really being silly. He was probably on his way to the beach again. Maybe he wanted to watch the sails in the evening wind.

He'd been in a car. She hadn't really seen it, but she had the impression of a small, open sports car. Something old and travel worn.

"Don't worry," Stanley said suddenly, reaching out

to cover her hands with his own large one. "We'll make sure she's back to normal in no time."

Perris gazed at him in surprise, then realized that he'd noticed her tension and attributed it to her mother's condition. A stab of guilt shot through her, but she smiled wanly and looked back out the window.

Robert Chase, she told herself firmly, I am putting you out of my mind. As of now.

"Look," Stan directed as they pulled into the parking lot at Jocko's. "There are Gary and Kathy."

Perris felt a flood of relief as she waved to the couple. Here were old friends, some of whom she hadn't seen for years. Once they all got together and talked over old times, she would feel a part of it again. She would feel as though she'd never been away. Then maybe these errant feelings would fade.

Gary was executive vice-president of a large electronics firm now, and Kathy, who'd once been Perris's best summer friend, was his wife and the mother of his two children. They and a number of her other friends from the old days had vacation homes at the lake. Some of the men commuted, only coming out from Los Angeles on weekends, while others had so many contacts there now that they were able to conduct business at the lake for as long as they pleased.

"We have a boy and a girl," Kathy told Perris once they'd been seated in the cozy dining hall. "Isn't that perfect? Just what we wanted."

Kathy was still schoolgirl cute with her mop of blond curls and her dancing gray eyes. She had the look of a satisfied woman. Perris hoped that she would look half as happy once she'd totally rejoined this crowd.

"Are you planning to have any more?" she asked innocently.

Kathy stared at her blankly. "Any more?" she asked. "But, Perris, no one has more than two."

"Oh." Chastised, Perris looked across the table at Gary. "I hadn't heard that they were rationed."

Gary grinned back at her. "Absolutely," he said, joining her in her joke. "So you'd better get in there and get your share while you're still allowed any at all."

She grinned back. She'd always liked Gary. He'd been a hot dog of a water-skier during summers past. Always getting into mischief.

Now, with his short, slicked-back brown hair and his growing paunch, he looked as settled as her parents had seemed to her in the old days.

But there was nothing wrong with that, her conscience argued sternly. That was exactly what her goal was, too. You're not a kid any longer, she told herself.

Jocko's was just the same. A nice little Italian restaurant with sparkling white tablecloths and crystal candle holders at each table, it had dancing to live music on weekend evenings, and as the band tuned up, Perris could tell that these musicians would play all the same tunes the bands had played during her college years.

As they ate their lasagna and gnocchi, men and women she had once known well arrived in twos, or sometimes in newly divorced singles, and the festive spirit swirled around her.

But somehow, as the others grew more and more animated, Perris began to feel more and more out of place. They were all so much the same. And those who had changed seemed to have lost something rather than gained. A feeling of unease was tickling the edges of her spirit. Was this really what she wanted?

"Hey, everybody. Remember how we used to dance?" Kathy had always been an enthusiastic dancer, and it seemed she hadn't changed a bit. "Let's get out there and show these people that we still know how to strut our stuff!"

Perris looked at Stan, and somehow she couldn't do

it. She loved to dance when the mood was right, but the mood was definitely off at the moment.

"I'm sorry, honey," she answered his invitation. "I think I'll sit here for a while."

He frowned at her, puzzled, but when Gary refused to join in, either, he found himself being dragged away by Kathy, leaving Perris to field the many questions from her friends alone.

"So you've finished your fiddle playing, have you?" round-faced Melody asked. "Ready to join the rest of us in the diaper set?"

"You'd better buy a place in Westwood first," Gary advised importantly. "Some choice land is coming on the market soon. I'll give Stan a call and get him in on it."

"You'll want to avoid Acapulco for your honeymoon this year," willowy Janey Strands told her emphatically. "The people showing up down there are strictly declassé." She made a face to illustrate just exactly what she meant. "The best people are going to Cabo San Lucas or Kauai in the Islands."

"No, listen," Melody chimed in. "Cruises. Everybody is into cruises now. I'm not kidding. They're so great. You don't have to do anything but eat and sleep."

"And maybe a little drinking on the side," Stan teased as he returned from the dance floor and slid in beside Perris. "Speaking of which, I could use a refill. How about the rest of you?"

Perris wondered if maybe Stan hadn't had enough already. She'd seen him down at least three mixed drinks as well as a good deal of wine with dinner.

"How about a walk along the shore instead?" she whispered to him, but he didn't seem to hear.

"Waitress, another round please," he ordered the harried-looking girl, who nodded and disappeared into the bar.

Perris sat back and listened to the conversation as it rose and fell around her. These were her friends; they had been for many years. Why was it that she felt so alienated from them? Was it because of her many years away? Or had she left in the first place because of these feelings?

Kathy and Gary were still favorites of hers, but something about their life didn't appeal to her as it should. And Janey—all she could talk about was what "the best people" did, not to mention that she was already divorced. Perris had watched as her beautiful blue eyes had taken in every man present, as though judging each in some sort of eligibility contest of her own. Was Janey being predatory or merely working for her own survival? It wasn't fair to judge when she didn't know all the reasons behind what these people did.

Time to snap out of this ennui, she told herself sharply. This was what her future held, and she'd better get used to it.

"Hello, Perris."

She knew even before she looked up that this wasn't yet another friend from the old days. But when she did raise her eyes to stare into Robert Chase's electric-blue gaze, she found the view as refreshing as a plunge into frosty lake waters.

"Hi," she said when she could manage it.

He was standing easily, his weight balanced, like a prize fighter about to leave his corner. When she spoke, his gaze left hers and traveled slowly around the silent table, stopping at each member of the party.

"Will you dance with me?" he asked her softly, looking at Stan.

She opened her mouth to refuse, but Stan beat her to it.

"She's not dancing tonight." He suddenly sounded

very pompous to Perris. "Especially not with strangers."

"But we're not strangers." Robert smiled and held his darkly tanned hand out to her. "Are we, Perris?"

His supreme confidence stunned her. She turned to Stan, ready to ask his permission, but she stopped when she saw the anger in his face.

"I said she wouldn't dance," Stan announced, as though Perris had no voice of her own. "She's busy talking to her friends. Take my word for it, she especially doesn't want to dance with you."

Perris's temper reared its head again. She'd spent the whole evening hearing about what someone in their "set" should and shouldn't do. Suddenly, she'd had enough.

"I've got a mind of my own, Stan," she said evenly. "I hope you haven't forgotten that." Slipping out from behind the table, she tilted her chin toward Robert. "I'd love to dance," she stated clearly.

She half expected him to gloat a bit, but he didn't waste any time on the others in her party. Instead, he held out an arm for her, then led her toward the dance floor. Wondering if he noticed the excited buzz that started up at the table as they were walking away, Perris felt her cheeks redden slightly.

She had begun to question herself as to just what she was doing when he turned and took her in his arms. She hadn't wanted to dance with him. In fact, she wished he hadn't shown up at all. But her temper had put her in an uncomfortable position once again.

"What a coincidence, you showing up here." She might as well try a little small talk.

He pulled back and grinned down at her. "This is no coincidence, Perris," he answered in amusement. "I only came because you're here."

There was a quiver starting somewhere deep in her

chest. "But . . . how could you know where I was?" she asked indignantly.

His wide shoulders moved in a careless shrug. "I followed you," he announced, as though surprised that she hadn't guessed.

"What?" She stared at him, aghast. "You mean, on the street . . . ?"

He nodded. "In my car," he filled in. "I saw you leaving your house with that stuffed shirt, and I thought I'd better come along and help you plan an escape."

"An escape?" Why did she feel like laughing? "What made you think I might want to escape?"

He pulled her in close again. His right hand came up under her hair, gently holding the nape of her neck, while his left hand closed over her wrist, pressing her fingers up against his chest.

He wasn't dressed in designer jeans and an expensive knit rugby shirt, as were the men in her party. But at least he was wearing more than ragged cutoffs. His jeans were old and tight, like a faded friend too well loved to be tossed out, even though it deserved to be. The shirt was chambray, but clean and crisp and open at the neck.

She could feel his warm breath in her hair, but then he pulled her even closer, and the warmth of his body blotted out everything else. His thighs pressed against hers as they moved about the floor. She found herself flexing her fingers against his chest, stretching them out to move almost in a caress, and suddenly his heartbeat was throbbing beneath her fingertips.

She caught her breath as she felt it. There was a magic in this man that seemed to flow around her like a liquid web, tangling her into something she wouldn't let happen if she could only think clearly enough to avoid it. When she felt his lips against her temple, instead of pulling away, she closed her eyes and sighed.

"Come with me," he was whispering into her ear.
"Come for a ride."

She drew back, opening her eyes, and looked him
full in the face. "You think you've got me softened up
and ready for anything, don't you?" she said scathingly.
"Well, think again, Robert Chase. The only reason I
agreed to dance with you was because I was angry with
Stan."

He whirled her into a spinning turn, then slowed the
pace again.

"I like you angry at Stan," he said placidly. "But just
think how much simpler it would be if there were no
Stan at all."

She frowned, struggling to keep her head pulled back
far enough for her to see his face. "What do you
mean?" she asked suspiciously.

His smile was beguiling. "You don't need Stan anymore. Now that you have me . . ."

"What?" Shock robbed her of speech, and her feet
stopped moving as she stood gaping at his calm confidence.

"People are staring," he warned, nudging her back
into the rhythm of the dance. "I don't care if you make
a scene, but somehow I have this feeling that you'd hold
it against me in the end."

"What do you mean, now that I have you?" she
whispered hoarsely. "I don't have you. I don't even
want you. . . ."

"Don't you?" There was no humor in his eyes now,
and as she gazed up into them, she seemed to be
moving deeper and deeper into their misty blue depths.

Suddenly, achingly, she knew that she wanted him
very much. The desire was deep and twisting, like
nothing she'd ever felt before, like nothing she had
known existed.

"Don't you, Perris?" His hand was moving along the

naked skin between her shoulder blades, then up again to cradle the back of her head. "Can't you feel how good we're going to be together?" he asked huskily. "Can't you feel the spell beginning?"

His hand snaked its way down her back until he found the very tip of her backbone. Spreading his fingers, he pressed firmly, drawing her hips in against his. She gasped as tiny sensations began to tremble in her legs, then up through her body.

"No," she protested desperately, shaking her head so that her thick hair swirled about her shoulders. "No, no, no."

She did feel it. She'd felt it from the first. But she knew that it spelled disaster for her. She knew that she had to fight against it with all her strength.

The buccaneering grin was back. He was so damned confident of his power over her! "Don't worry, Perris," he said softly into her hair as he pulled her in against him again. "I'm not going to do anything to hurt you."

"How do you know what will hurt me?" she ground out against his chest. Then, with a bit more spirit, she added, "You couldn't hurt me if you tried!"

"Good," he said approvingly. "Then we're agreed."

She stared up at him, her dark eyes glowing. "Just what is it that you think we're in agreement on?" she asked crisply. "I hope you know, because I haven't the foggiest notion."

The music had changed sometime before from the slow ballad that had been playing when they first took the floor to the heavy beat of a rock tune, but he still held her in the same full arm embrace and still moved her about the room in the same style. Somehow he managed to keep time to the music while making flagrant love to her with his eyes and his body.

"Our relationship, of course," he answered her sarcastic question. "It's always better to get the ground rules down early. Otherwise, disappointments are bound to arise.''

She couldn't decide whether she wanted to laugh or cry. He was so supremely sure of himself, and so very wrong. As the ragged beat faded away, he continued to move her in a rhythmic sway, looking down at her.

"The dance is over," she reminded him finally. "Don't you think you'd better take me back to my table?"

"Back to good old Stan?" He grimaced. "Why not come with me now? Why waste time?"

She shook her head in despair. "You don't seem to be getting this. I'm not going with you at all."

His white teeth flashed in an indulgent smile. "Okay. I'll give you a little more time to think it over."

Slowly, he disentangled his arms and began to lead her back to her seat.

When they reached the table, she couldn't resist the question. "Just how much time have I got?" she asked.

"About twelve hours." His smile wrapped around her like a sensuous cloak of soft, thick fur. "But it will be hard for me to wait that long."

She stared into his eyes, noting the laughter but unable to take it as a joke. He wanted her. She could see that. And he meant to have her. A tiny shiver worked its way along her spine.

3

~eeeeeeeee~

She might have stood there for hours just gazing up into his eyes, but with a quirk of one corner of his wide mouth, he set her free, turning to look at the startled people sitting around her table.

"Thanks for the dance, Perris," he told her, nodding casually to the others. Then he turned and strolled away, leaving her to take her seat by herself.

A quick glance at Stan showed that he'd been sulking for the entire time. She could hardly blame him, but she wasn't sure what she could do to mollify him.

"Where did you pick him up?" he asked as soon as Robert was out of earshot. "I can't believe the things you do sometimes."

"There's nothing wrong with him," she answered, surprising herself with her defensiveness. "He happens to be a very nice man."

Stan scowled. "Tell her, Gary," he said sourly. "Tell her who her 'very nice man' happens to be."

Perris glanced quickly at the others at the table, surprised that they might know something about Robert that she didn't. But then, what *did* she know? Practically nothing.

"He's just a bum, Perris," Gary was saying, his brow furled with worry. "You really shouldn't fool around with a fellow like that."

She looked from one condemning face to another. "And just what exactly makes you think that he's a bum?" she asked tartly.

Gary squared his shoulders with self-importance. "He's been hanging around for about a month. He came as a caretaker for old Mrs. Castlemeyer's place."

Mrs. Castlemeyer was one of the original residents of the area. Because of an asthmatic condition, she spent most of every year in the dry desert air. She had built herself a mansion that stood just at the edge of Havapai Shore, a little apart from the condominiums. It was rumored that her money came from the old days of the Comstock Lode in Virginia City, Nevada, but no one knew the truth. All anyone was sure of was that she was a dear old lady who always seemed to relish a visit and a chance to talk but who didn't seem to have any family or friends other than the people she knew at Havapai Shore.

"Where is Mrs. Castlemeyer?" Perris asked. "What does she say about it all?"

"She hasn't come out yet," Kathy burst in. "There's nothing really wrong with the man. It's just . . . well, he's only a caretaker, after all."

They were all staring at her as if that last fact had proven their case. Perris shrugged. "A caretaker is a human being, too," she said easily. "Personally, I don't really care, anyway."

Smiling brightly at Kathy, she made an obvious attempt at changing the subject. "Tell me about your new jet boat, Kathy. Gary tells me you can pull ten skiers at a time with it."

The evening seemed to last forever. Though she tried to keep her mind off him, Perris couldn't seem to stop thinking about her handsome stranger. She turned to search the crowd for his blond head so often that Stan began to notice and even made a comment.

"You're awfully restless tonight, Perris," he snapped. "Can't you relax?"

"Maybe she's missing her European adventures," Kathy said, giggling. "How about it, Perris? Do you wish you could've stayed over there?"

Perris smiled and shook her head. "No," she answered firmly. "No, it was definitely time for me to come home."

"You can say that again," Stan affirmed. "And now that you're here, we're going to make sure you don't get out of our sight. Aren't we?" His smile invited the agreement of everyone else at the table, and they all chimed in enthusiastically.

"That's right, Perris," Gary stated. "We're going to make you one of us again."

Perris smiled her gratitude to them all, but something inside her was squirming. What if she didn't want to be one of them? What if she only wanted to be herself, Perris Fleming, and whatever that entailed? Could they accept her that way? Or could they only accept carbon copies of themselves?

Stan kissed her later outside the double doors of her condominium. "Tomorrow night we'll have dinner at my place," he told her firmly. "My parents aren't coming out until August, so we'll have it all to ourselves whenever we want it."

Perris tried to smile back at his meaningful glance. She knew exactly what he was planning for the next day. She only wished she could work up a little enthusiasm about it. After all, this was the man she was planning to marry. There ought to be a spark between them. Some excitement.

Tomorrow night. Maybe that was when it would begin. Maybe when they were alone, when he made love to her as a lover, the spark would take fire.

The trouble was, she could already feel it burning by just thinking about Robert Chase. And that wouldn't do. No, that wouldn't do at all.

Perris left her drapes open, so when she woke up in the morning, her first sight was the stunning blue of the Arizona sky. When she sat up in her bed, she could add the black outline of the jagged mountains, then the red-gold of the desert waste, and finally, the emerald green of the carefully watered lawn that ran between the two rows of condominiums. The colors were vividly alive, and she felt compelled to jump up and join the day.

A quick shower drove the last remnants of sleep from her body. She admired her new tan in the full-length mirror that covered one entire side of her bathroom. Only small strips of white skin were left at the most strategic areas of her body. She grinned, wondering if she should find a private cove and work on those.

But for now she was not about to walk around her mother's house naked. Instead, she pulled a floor-length robe of translucent cotton gauze from her closet. Quickly, she tied the belt of the lemon-yellow garment; then she was off down the stairs, ready for breakfast.

The kitchen had been well stocked by the woman who came every morning at ten, and Perris set out eggs and bacon, along with fresh bread for toast. There was no sign of her mother yet, and she wondered if she should go into her bedroom and check on her.

No, she thought, stretching dreamily, she would let

her sleep as long as she could. Meanwhile, Perris would find something to do to keep herself busy. She wandered into the living room and looked out at the lake. In the early-morning calm, the water looked as pale as blue silk, but there wasn't much to hold her in the view. She went back to the kitchen. There was a newspaper lying by the front door, but she didn't feel like reading about all the disasters of the previous day. Something restless was gnawing at her.

She knew she would be able to still it if only she could run up and practice her music. But that would be the worst way to wake her mother. Instead, she had an inspiration. Why not make some fresh-squeezed orange juice for breakfast?

They had no trees in their own little enclosed garden, but there was a whole mini-orchard of them in the green belt that bordered their property. Perris bit her lip as she looked down at her light robe, wondering if she should bother to run up and change first. But it was early. No one would be about. Why not chance it? With a daring grin, she turned to leave by the back way.

She pulled open the sliding-glass door and held back the heavy drapes so that she could slip out through the little yard, then through the heavy wooden gate and into the public park behind the house. The stretch of green ran the length of the development, and the well-kept trees hid the rows of houses from one another. A fountain at one end sparkled with a constant flow of precious water, while a rose-covered gazebo opened onto the little stand of orange trees. It was a beautiful place, little used by the residents, who generally stayed in their air-conditioned rooms unless they were out on the lake in their cruisers. Perris seemed to have it to herself.

The bright orange fruits looked like jewels set against the shiny dark green leaves. Reaching up, Perris snapped one orange after another from their brittle stems until her arms were full. It was as she turned back toward the house, carefully balancing her harvest, that she saw him.

He was sitting on the stone bench near the edge of the grove, in the shadow of a twisting juniper. She must have walked right past him on her way out.

"Hi," he said.

"Oh!" she answered, and the oranges went flying in every direction.

He smiled, and she stood looking at him for a long moment.

"It hasn't been twelve hours," she whispered.

His laugh was low and sensual. "I told you it would be too long to wait," he said. His gaze dropped to make a sensual journey across her breasts, the nipples barely visible beneath the filmy cloth of her robe, and she forced herself not to hide from his examination.

When he stood and came toward her, she automatically backed away. The sun seemed to glint in his hair as it fell over his forehead, making shadows where the grooves lined his face. She stared at his dark hand as he reached for her, at the clean, square-cut nails, at the strength in his fingers.

"Entirely too long." His hand cupped the back of her head and pulled her closer. Slowly, his face lowered until his lips were tasting hers so softly that she could barely feel his touch. But his breath was a warm breeze against her cheek, and she sighed as he drew back again.

"Good morning." He was smiling, always smiling. She couldn't help but smile back.

He looked down at the spilled fruit. "You're a bit clumsy in the morning, aren't you?" he teased, leaning down to help her collect her bounty and stack it on the little patio table. "What are these? They don't look much like the oranges I'm used to."

"These are grown a lot in Arizona. They're called Moros," she replied. "And also blood oranges." She tried to balance them, dropping two again in her hurry. "I'd show you how they got that name if I had a knife and a place to use for a table."

"Come on." He took the oranges from her and led her up the steps into the gazebo. "There's a stone table in here." He plopped the fruit down on it. "And I just happen to have a pocket knife with me."

She looked at him as he bent to pry the knife from the hard-to-reach slit in his tight-fitting jeans. He wore a plaid cotton shirt that was open at the neck, revealing his golden chest hair as well as his mahogany tan. She found herself looking away nervously, wishing that her blood wasn't singing in her veins.

"Here." She handed him an orange. "Cut it open."

He did as she suggested and smiled at the bright red fruit revealed within the orange skin. Raising the cuplike half to his lips, he took a quick taste. "Delicious," he approved. "When's breakfast?"

Biting her lower lip, she tried to stiffen her resolve. "I'll have to get back, and you'll have to leave," she attempted, but was stopped by his low laugh.

"You've got to be kidding," he scoffed. "Now that I've seen paradise, there's no way you're going to make me leave it behind."

He cupped her head with both hands, then slid them down her neck until they rested just underneath the opening of her robe. "Anyone with any manners, or better still, any heart, would invite me in to breakfast."

The sparkle in his blue eyes told her that he had something on his mind other than food, but she tried to ignore it.

"I'm not going to invite you in at all," she told him

truthfully. She could just imagine how her mother would react to someone like him! Especially when she'd found him lurking around in the green belt at six in the morning.

"Then we'll just have to stay out here," he answered good-naturedly.

His teeth flashed white against his tan skin, and she watched as he came toward her. They were in the gazebo, in the center of the development, yet protected from view by the thick growth of yellow climbing roses that spread out across the wooden structure. She knew his intention, and she knew that she wouldn't resist. Not completely.

This time his lips met hers with a purpose, and she found herself responding without reservation. The silky-smooth movement of his mouth against hers was something she'd never felt before. His mouth was hard with intent, yet gloved in velvet, seductive and implacable all at once.

She felt his hands slip beneath her robe at the same time that his tongue penetrated her mouth, and she tried to move away, but when he felt her retreat, his fingers tightened on her flesh, drawing her closer, and with a moan, she abandoned the effort.

It was infinitely sweeter to let him guide this moment, to feel his tongue exploring her, to feel his hands working across her naked back. She found her arms sliding effortlessly around his neck, her fingers reaching for his thick blond hair, her body arching against his to catch every delicious sensation.

"Mmm, that's the way I knew you'd feel," he murmured into her ear as he pressed her ever closer. "Just think of the night we might have had . . . but never mind. We'll make up for it with a day you won't soon forget."

So this was what it would be like, she thought lazily to

herself as she closed her eyes, letting the tiny quivers his tongue produced against the skin of her neck shiver through her body. This was what it would be like to be the sort of woman Robert was obviously used to. She would go with him now, spend the day. They would make love, revel gloriously in the desire that sprang between them so easily. They might lie together on some sunny hillside, taking and giving as the mood demanded, running down to bathe in the cool waters of the lake, then heading back up to a shady spot where their passion would swell again, swell and be assuaged by their mutual lovemaking.

The picture was lovely. But the picture was of some other woman. Not of her.

Slowly, with exquisite reluctance, her fingers slid free of the rich wealth of his hair, and she brought her hands down to push against his chest.

"Stop, Robert," she whispered. "Enough."

His laugh was a low rumble against her neck. "Don't be absurd," he whispered into the hollow of her neck. "If you think this is enough, then you've never been loved as you deserve to be."

That triggered her anger. "And I suppose you're the master lover, aren't you?" she retorted, her tone hard with sarcasm. "You're the one who will awaken all my hidden passion." She pulled back sharply. "What bunk!"

Her words and struggle were strong enough to give him pause, and he raised his head to gaze curiously into her angry eyes.

"Heard it before, have you?" he asked, laughter still glinting in his blue eyes.

"A hundred times." Her anger died in the face of his response. How could she stay angry at a man who didn't seem to take himself so seriously that every jab was a slight to his manhood? It had been her experience that most men did; most men seemed to look for insults where none were intended. To find a man who could laugh them off was a rarity.

She shrugged out of his embrace but didn't move away. Some magnetism seemed to hold her in his sphere.

"Look," she began, then hesitated, unable to meet his eyes. How was she going to phrase this? After the way she'd reacted to his kisses, how could she tell him that she was engaged to marry another man?

Biting her lower lip, she summoned her courage and raised her head to look him in the face. "You really must leave," she told him earnestly. "And you mustn't do this sort of thing anymore."

His grin had a touch of cynicism. "You use the word 'must' a lot, don't you?" he asked softly.

"It's a perfectly good word," she defended herself. "It has to do with rules and proprieties."

Suddenly, the smile was gone from his eyes. It was as though a summer storm had darkened the blue depths.

"'Rules and proprieties,'" he repeated slowly. "Those are nothing but guidelines made by people." His lips curved, but there was still no smile in his eyes. "We're people, too, Perris. We can make our own rules."

She'd known that he'd be like this from the first, hadn't she? She'd known he wasn't her type, that he wouldn't fit in with her life. She had to get him out of her mind, and the sooner the better.

Taking a deep breath, she made the announcement that she knew would squelch any further problems. "I'm engaged to marry Stan Fremont," she declared almost harshly.

"I know," he answered without hesitation.

She stared at him. "You know?" she repeated dumbly.

He nodded. "Your friend Stanley came to visit me last night."

She knew how silly she must look standing before him with her mouth hanging open, but she couldn't hold back her incredulous reaction.

"Stan came to see you?" She still couldn't believe it. "What for?"

"To warn me off, of course." He looked at her as though she'd turned out to be a bit denser than he'd expected. "I knew he'd come the moment I saw you two together."

"Stan did that?" She tried to picture the confrontation between the two of them, but it wouldn't come into focus. "What did he say?"

Robert lounged back against the woven wood of the walled gazebo. Lids lowered, he seemed to be assessing how she would take what he was telling her. "Stanley told me that you and he had practically been betrothed at birth. That he'd waited lo these many years and was not about to get rooked out of his investment after all this time."

Perris's smile was thin. "A very free translation, I've no doubt," she scoffed.

He didn't answer her accusation. "That's what came across. With the minor addendum that I wasn't good enough for you. I would only drag you through the dirt and make you unfit to be his wife."

She returned his solemn stare. "And what did you tell him?" she asked breathlessly.

"I told him that engagements were made to be broken. That you were fair game until he got his gold band around your throat."

She winced at the bitterness of his tone. "You don't think much of marriage and commitment, do you?" she asked softly.

He grimaced. "More rules. I can do without them."

Yes, she'd known that from the beginning. It was written all over him. She took a deep, shuddering breath. "Then you'd better go," she whispered.

For a long, tenuous moment, their gazes locked in silent battle, forceful masculine intent against feminine resistance. Perris felt herself tremble and knew he could overcome her if he chose. But would he? Somehow he seemed to be holding back, waiting for some sign.

Finally, he spoke. "Haven't you ever wanted to break the rules, Perris?" he asked with a low, silky sensuality. "Wouldn't you like to find out what it's like to risk it all for something you really want? To catch the wind in your sails and go with it?"

She shook her head, suddenly frightened. "No," she answered quickly. "No."

His blue gaze swept across her body once again, and he erased the distance between them with one smooth movement, then deftly opened the belt of her robe, letting the two sides fall away to reveal her naked body before she even realized his intention.

"I'm going to teach you how to sail, Perris," he growled, holding back her instinctive move to cover herself, "whether you want to learn or not."

He pulled her robe down from her shoulders so that it barely hung on at her elbows. Perris had stopped struggling. In a sort of daze, she watched as he looked at her body, not moving, not thinking, only marveling at the worship in his eyes.

"You're beautiful," he told her huskily, placing his hand in the valley between her breasts and spreading his fingers to nudge them both into a gentle swaying motion. "Look at yourself," he ordered. "Look at how beautiful you are."

Obediently, she looked down and saw his dark hand against her light skin, saw how her nipples were swelling into dusky peaks as they caught the morning breeze, saw how her body seemed to move toward him of its own accord.

"And you want to hold yourself back with rules?" he whispered. Then he lowered his head, gently taking one nipple with his tongue, coaxing it even tighter.

A moan began deep in her throat as she felt the trembling in her legs. Something buried in her soul was stirring, something she had never felt before.

"Robert . . ." she protested, but it came out in a tiny whisper that was lost in the breeze.

His warm hands were gliding along her sides, curling in about her hips, cupping her, holding her, moving her closer to his hard body, and she found her hands twisting in his thick hair once again, pulling his head harder against her breast, arching to bring more of her flesh into contact with his.

She knew this was insane. She was engaged to Stan. Why was this stranger in her arms? Why was he the one who had the magic that could stir her to this mad hunger?

As he pressed her hips against his, she could feel the growing hunger in him, too, and her blood raced with excitement.

"Oh, Robert," she groaned, meaning to tell him to stop but not capable of going beyond his name.

His mouth on hers was sweet and hot with desire. As he made himself felt in every sensitive corner of her soul, she found herself moving with him, following his lead, matching his rising heat with a flame of her own.

Suddenly, he was rearing back, staring at her as though he were as surprised by what was happening between them as she was.

His blond hair was falling in brightly colored shafts over his blue eyes, shadowing his craggy face. His strong fingers tightened along her rib cage, holding her firmly away from him while his gaze searched hers.

"What is it?" she whispered, confused. "What's the matter?"

An uneven grin curled his wide mouth. "I'm not sure," he admitted ruefully. Something flickered deep in his gaze. "You almost scare me, Perris Fleming," he said softly. "I get the feeling maybe you're going to teach me as much as I'm going to teach you."

She had to gather her strength. Though he leaned down to kiss her breast gently again, she steeled herself not to respond and began pulling her robe back around her shoulders.

"You must go, Robert," she said. "And I use the word 'must' advisedly."

He drew her into his arms and nuzzled along her neck, but she forced herself to remain ramrod stiff despite the electricity shooting sparks through her system.

"What Stan told you is correct," she went on, trying to ignore the tremor in her voice. "We're engaged. I'm going to marry him. And you are going to leave us alone!"

Reluctantly, he realized that she was adamant. In slow, tender stages, he began to disentangle his body from hers.

"I'll certainly have no trouble leaving Stanley alone," he agreed. "But you are another matter."

There was no smile in his eyes, only a deep, troubled promise.

"You, I won't leave alone," he told her solemnly. "Not ever."

She tied the sash of her robe, avoiding his disturbing glance.

"Good-bye, Robert," she said firmly, taking up as many oranges as she could easily handle and leaving the rest. She hurried down the stairs of the gazebo, then forced herself to walk more slowly across the width of the green to her own back gate. But all the time she felt his examination, and it took a supreme effort to keep from turning to look at him as she made her way in through her sliding-glass door, pushing aside the billowing drapes. She had a problem here, and she knew it.

4

~~~~~~~~~~~~~~~

As Perris water-skied across the lake behind Gary's boat white spray stung her eyes, but that didn't blind her to the identity of the man sailing the catamaran they were skimming by. Only about four hours had passed since that same tall body had been holding her in an embrace that still brought a catch to her breathing when she thought of it.

He saw her, too, but neither waved. He was making his way slowly, meandering with the vagaries of the breeze, toward the remote beach where she and the others had their blankets and equipment set up. What was he planning to do once he got there?

She hadn't a doubt that he knew just what he was doing, that he'd seen their camp and was heading that way on purpose. How would Stan react to another surprise visit from Robert? She decided that the best thing to do would be to make sure neither she nor Stan was around once he'd arrived.

She signaled to Stan, who was watching from the back of the boat, that she wanted to go in toward shore, and the sleek, cherry-red craft turned its sharp nose toward the beach and swung her in. She timed her release perfectly, dropping the tow rope and feeling herself cruise toward the sandy shore, sinking slowly, so that she landed in very shallow water and had only to release the fittings on her skis to walk up on the dry sand.

"Hey, that was nice," Kathy greeted her warmly. "Haven't lost your touch, I see."

Perris picked up her skis and walked back up to where the chairs and blankets had been arranged under the canopy that let them enjoy the openness of the lake without having to endure the pounding sun. Janey Strands lay out away from the canopy on a bright blue towel, getting a tan on her long, willowy body, while Kathy's two children, a boy of three and a baby girl, slept quietly in a playpen in the shade.

The scene was reminiscent of so many scenes from the summers of a few years before when Perris and her friends had spent hours lazing on one beach or another, water-skiing or sailing or just working on the perfect tan. She'd been glad to come. Friends from Los Angeles had arrived for a visit and were keeping her mother occupied, so Perris had the entire day to enjoy.

Stan and Gary had brought the boat in and tied it to a float near the shore by the time Perris had toweled her hair semidry. She'd put a light beach coat on over her electric-blue, one-piece suit and tied it at the waist. There weren't many boats on the lake yet, and looking down across the water, she could see the bright rainbow-colored sail of Robert's catamaran coming closer all the time.

"Why don't we make a run up the river?" she

suggested impulsively. "Just like we used to do in the old days."

"Oh," Kathy cried, her face radiant. "Why don't we? You know, Gary proposed to me up the river. Remember that old green ski boat he had then? We took it all the way up to Davis Dam, and Gary popped the question on the way."

"Great." Perris began to gather her things, pleased with her plan. "Let's go relive old times."

Stan and Gary agreed. "I haven't been up the river for ages," Stan said. "I'd like to see what kind of development they've done around Needles and Bullhead City."

But Kathy shook her head sadly. "I can't leave the kids," she said wistfully. "You go and tell me how it was."

"Oh, Kathy." Perris looked at the two little toddlers and knew that the trip would be too long for them. "Janey will stay with them. Won't you, Janey?"

Janey raised her sleepy face to nod in slow agreement, then dropped down again, her blond hair a mop of platinum about her.

"You see?" Perris told her friend.

But Kathy still shook her head. "I wouldn't leave my kids with her," she told Perris softly, making sure that Janey couldn't hear her. "She's liable to take out after the first man she sees and forget all about them."

Perris looked over the water. The rainbow sail was coming closer. She could discern Robert's form leaning out over the water to counterbalance the wind in the sail.

"Why don't we go in shifts?" Stan suggested. "Kathy can come with us now, and Perris can stay with the kids. Then we'll come back and trade Kathy for Perris in an hour or so."

"Great," Kathy exclaimed before Perris had a chance to change the order of travel. "That would be best, since they're both asleep now. I'll be back by the time they wake up from their naps." She looked anxiously at Perris. "You don't mind, do you? Really, I can't depend on Janey. You or Melody, yes, but Janey?" She shrugged. "Is it okay?"

Perris forced a smile. "Of course it is. But get going, all of you. I'm going to be ready for more skiing by the time you get back."

She watched them clamber into the red boat and waved them off, then turned to watch the catamaran arrive at the shore. Robert jumped out and pulled his graceful double-hulled boat up onto the sand, then turned to look at Perris. His blue eyes met hers innocently and held her gaze for a long moment, but neither of them smiled or spoke. She wished she could frown and order him off, but she couldn't. He'd caught her in his web once more.

He was wearing only cutoffs again, and the sun turned his tan skin to creamy mocha. The hair on his legs was almost silver in the glistening sunlight, while the hair on his chest was a burnished copper.

What incredible timing, she thought ruefully. Even now, if Stan looked around, he would see what was going on behind his back and return in a rage.

Behind his back. That was really what this was, wasn't it? Even though she'd tried to avoid it, here it was. Perris felt a wave of disbelief that she could be involved in something so underhanded. In fact, she refused to be. With one resentful glare at Robert, who was making his cat fast a dozen yards away, she turned, kicked up a spray of sand and strode back toward the children she was supposed to be watching.

Of course they were awake. There was some magic

bell in a small child's head that went off whenever his mother got too far away, and Perris spent the next few minutes soothing the boy and rocking the baby, reassuring them both that they hadn't been abandoned.

She felt rather than heard Robert coming up behind her, but she refused to turn and greet him. Instead, she handed the little boy a cup of juice and took the baby to her chest, soothing her with soft nonsense words.

"Are these yours?" His deep voice was warm with amusement.

She threw a quick glance over her shoulder and met his blue eyes for only a fraction of a second. "What if they are? Would that make a difference?"

"Why should it? I like kids." He came around the other side of the playpen and grinned down at Tommy, the little boy. "I used to be one myself, you know."

Now she couldn't avoid meeting his eyes, and with that bond came the smile she couldn't hold back when she looked at him. "What makes you think you've grown up?" she asked him softly.

Suddenly, his eyes darkened, and she was struck once again at how quickly his mercurical moods could change. "I grew up, Perris. I was as old as the hills once. But I found I didn't like it much, so I went back to being a kid again." His grin returned. "Now I'm having much more fun. And I'm going to make you try it, too."

"No." She shook her head slowly. "I don't want to be a kid again. I've done my growing up, and I deserve to be an adult for a change."

He laughed. "Take it from me; you won't like it." He reached out to brush a strand of hair from her eyes, his fingers grazing her skin so lightly that she almost raised her face to his hand to get more of his touch.

"Come on," he said huskily. "Come for a sail with me."

Catch the wind in your sails and go with it, he'd told

her only that morning. Now he was offering her a chance to do just that.

She shook her head, avoiding his eyes. "I have children to watch," she said, her voice without expression.

He hesitated for a moment. "We'll take them along."

She looked at him, surprised, and he answered with a grin.

"I told you. I like kids."

She searched his eyes for a moment, then shook her head again. "No."

"I've got my sailboard with me. Come on out and try it."

"I don't know how to sail one of those things," she said evasively.

"I'll teach you." His hand had settled on her naked shoulder. "I'll teach you everything you need to know."

She hugged the baby more tightly to her chest and rocked her. "I don't need you to teach me anything," she told him, her voice low, her eyes on the horizon. "I want you out of my life. That's all."

There was the sound of a throat being cleared behind them. Janey was making her presence known.

"Are you offering free wind-surfing lessons?" she asked, her voice provocative.

Perris turned to look at her. Janey was still flat on her towel in the sand, but sometime in the previous few minutes she'd unhooked the top of her suit and let it drop away, so that she was now displaying a long, lovely, naked back, from the top of her spine to very near the end of it. Only a slim strip of turquoise cloth covered her rounded bottom. As they watched, she raised herself up on her elbows, holding her towel against her chest with pretended modesty. "I've always wanted to learn how to handle one of those things."

Perris turned back to the children, embarrassed for

the poor girl. Of all the transparent ploys, this was the worst she'd ever seen. To her amazement, however, Robert was leaving her side, moving toward Janey.

"Come on, then," he was saying. "I'll teach you all about it."

Something was flooding Perris's chest, some sort of wild confusion that she couldn't quite identify. She looked down at Tommy and handed him a toy he'd thrown out of the playpen, then began rocking the baby again. Little Sherry felt so warm in her arms and smelled so clean. She clung to the child, trying to avoid noticing what was happening a few yards away.

But she couldn't block it out. Sneaking a quick glance, she saw just what she'd suspected. Robert was leaning down to help Janey back into the halter of her bathing suit, and she was giggling and looking back at him from beneath her long lashes. He smiled back, and holding out a hand to her, helped her to her feet.

"Just let me put my things away," Janey said, and Robert nodded, going down to the edge of the water to unstrap and rig the sailboard.

Janey came in under the canopy to put away her towel and lotions. Her bright blue eyes met Perris's, and she bit her lip before speaking defensively. "Listen, girl, if you're going to throw that fish back into the water, I can catch him in my net, can't I?"

Perris held back the first sharp retort that came flying to her lips. "It's nothing to me," she said stiffly instead. "You know that Stan and I are engaged."

"That's what I was thinking." Janey stowed her towel in her bag and yanked the zipper closed. "So you won't mind if I move in and see what I can do."

Perris minded very much, but what could she say? She shook her head. "Of course not. Only . . ." She thought suddenly of the snobbish things she'd heard from Janey the night before. "He isn't really your type, is he? I mean, I thought you were after a potential husband. This one doesn't even have a decent job."

She gritted her teeth, internally chastising herself for what she'd just said. She really knew nothing about the man. How dare she say things like this just to warn Janey off?

But Janey merely shrugged her elegantly slim shoulders. She looked down the beach to where Robert was working with the rainbow sail, attaching it to the hinge that held it to the surfboardlike hull to form the sailboard. "No, he's not exactly 'till death do us part' material, is he?" She smiled, her tongue touching her lip in a feline gesture. "But look at him. Isn't he a hunk? He'll certainly do to fill in the spaces until my millionaire comes along."

Perris watched as Janey walked slowly down to meet Robert. The woman knew how to make full use of her assets. She was taking her time, making sure that Robert had a full chance to take in her long, graceful beauty as she came toward him. Perris saw Robert's smile and then turned away. She certainly wasn't going to watch them. She wasn't even going to think about them. She would play with the baby, instead.

She drew the child from where it nestled against her chest and found that the little girl was sound asleep again. With her fine white-blond curls and sleeping face, she looked angelic, and Perris smiled as she set her down on her little camping bed and turned to her brother.

But Tommy had no patience with Perris's attempts to get him to play. He was lining his small metal cars from one end of the playpen to the other.

"Don't talk to me," he warned her sternly, his brow wrinkled with seriousness. "I got to finish my cars."

Perris sighed and plopped down into a chair, reaching for a magazine. She tried to concentrate, but she couldn't even see the pictures as she flipped the pages. They blurred before her eyes as she listened to the cries coming from the water. Learning to wind surf seemed to be an awfully noisy process.

She snuck one glance at them, then wished she hadn't. They were close to shore, both of them standing on the board, and Robert had one hand on the rig and one arm around Janey's slim body, keeping her from skidding off the edge. As Perris watched, Janey screamed and turned, clutching Robert's waist with both hands, and with a shout of laughter, the two of them fell into the water while the sail dipped in on the opposite side.

Somehow the laughter cut the deepest. Perris flung herself out of the chair and threw herself belly down onto a blanket, facing away from the shore. The reason for the burning sensation that sliced through her like jagged lightning was finally clear to her. She was jealous.

She closed her eyes and pounded her fist into the warm sand, gritting her teeth and hating herself. She was jealous. She couldn't stand to see Janey's long fingers on Robert's skin, couldn't stand to think of how well her tall body looked standing next to his muscular form. The sound of their laughter blending in the desert breeze grated on her nerves like chalk on a blackboard.

The crunch of tires on the rocky road nearby drew her attention. A Peugeot stopped, and Melody jumped out, waving before she began to unpack her two children.

"We finally made it," she said as she came near, arms full of picnic basket and towels. "Greg will be along later. He had to play golf with a client this morning, but he promised he'd get away as soon as he could."

Perris rose, a brittle smile on her face. "Nice to see you. What darling children."

"Kevin and Keith, meet Perris Fleming." Melody had a casual attitude that made her seem to skim through life.

The two little boys had identical faces, each covered with freckles. They looked up at Perris, and she felt a quiver of apprehension. Their sparkling blue eyes looked like trouble to her. But what did she know about children, anyway?

"The others have gone for a run up the river. They should be back in an hour or so."

Melody didn't seem to hear her. She was shading her eyes and gazing out into the water. "Isn't that the fellow from last night at Jocko's?" she asked. "What's he doing here?"

She dropped her things and rummaged in her bag for sunglasses, which she affixed firmly to her nose. Then she turned to look at him again. "And that's Janey with him. Men follow her like bees after honey." She chuckled, settling down in a chair. "What a morning! I deserve a good ski run. Hope the lake doesn't get too choppy before they get back."

Perris was watching the two in the water. Robert was helping Janey back up on the board, but she was clinging to him, pretending to be frightened. Perris felt something explode inside her. She no longer cared about what she should do. She knew what she had to do.

She turned away from the water and stared up at the dark, brooding mountains that rimmed the basin. Did she dare take the chance?

"Melody." She turned toward her friend. "Kathy left her children with me, but you'll watch them for me, won't you?"

Melody looked up in surprise. "Sure. But where are you going?"

"I'm not certain," Perris muttered, rising to strip off

her beach coat and kick off her thongs. "That's what we're going to find out."

But she'd been a little too slow. As she turned, she saw Janey and Robert already walking up the beach toward the canopy. The sailboard had been folded down into its neat package, and Robert was carrying the hull under his arm.

"He is handsome, isn't he?" Melody murmured. "A little dangerous, though. I'd leave him to Janey if I were you."

I wish I could, Perris thought to herself, watching as he came near, his brown body glistening with water.

"That was such fun," Janey gushed, sliding a vamping look Robert's way. "But it's harder than it looks."

"Would you like to give it a try?"

Perris looked up eagerly as she heard him ask the question, but her heart fell when she saw that it was directed not at her but at Melody. If she had to wait through another lesson like the one he'd just given Janey, she would have to leave the beach.

"Not me." Melody laughed. "I'll stick to water-skiing."

"You should sit down and have a drink," Janey cooed. "You must be all worn out by now. Here." She pulled a chair through the sand for him. "Sit in this and I'll wait on you." She giggled. "Better take me up on that fast. I don't often make that sort of offer."

Robert smiled at Janey but shook his head. "I came out to sail, not to sit," he said quietly. "I'm going to take my cat out across the bay and try the wind surfing on the other side." He adjusted his grip on the sailboard; then, finally, his eyes met Perris's. "Want to come along?" he asked softly.

"Yes." She surprised even herself with the vehemence of her statement, and he grinned with pleasure.

"Let's go."

Janey frowned. "What should we tell Stan?" she whispered.

Perris laughed. A strange lightness was rushing through her. "Tell him I went for a sailboarding lesson, just like you did."

The sand was crisp and warm under her feet. She had to walk quickly to keep up with Robert's long strides. He didn't say a word to her until he'd lashed the sailboard to the craft and helped her aboard the canvas trampoline that bridged the twin hulls of the catamaran.

"Hold tight," he warned her as he pushed off, then jumped onto the deck himself. Taking the sheets in his hands, he leaned out over the hull and they got underway.

There was only a light wind blowing, but the sail of the small cat caught every scrap of it, and they sped along, skimming the water like a low-flying bird. Perris threw back her head, delighting in the wind that tossed her hair high behind her. It seemed like magic. There was hardly a sound, yet they were hurtling across the lake. Excitement surged in her, and she turned to smile at Robert.

"This is wonderful," she told him.

"Of course it is." He made an adjustment in the angle of the sail and leaned out farther over the water. "Now maybe you'll take my word about other things, too."

She turned her face away and let the spray wash over her. She was with him even though she shouldn't be. She would let him teach her something about wind surfing. But she wouldn't let him hold her as he had that morning. She wouldn't kiss him the way she had. She must be very careful that neither of them became caught up in that wild spell again.

"That's our destination."

She looked in the direction he was pointing and saw a small cove lined with white sand. It looked lonely with the stark black landscape behind it. Perris stared at it as they came closer, wondering why she felt a certain dread. Robert pulled the sail in, and the light craft came to a gradual stop near the shore. He hopped over the side and dragged it toward a bottle floating in the water.

The large brown bottle had a rope tied to it. He maneuvered the cat until it came close enough for him to grab the float and tie up to it.

"Did you put that float here?" Perris asked curiously.

"I did. I tied it to a very large rock on the bottom, so we'll have no worries about the cat drifting away."

She sat back and watched him work. "You must come here often."

He nodded his blond head. "This is my favorite cove, and I generally have it all to myself."

She let her fingers dangle languidly in the cool water. "What's it called?" she asked lazily, wanting to stay on board, to enjoy the gentle rocking and the warm sun.

He grinned and pulled himself back up on the canvas. "I call it Chase Haven. I don't know what the official name is."

She shook her head in mock exasperation. "You sure do claim a lot of territory around here," she accused. "First Havapai Shore is your own private beach; now this cove is yours as well."

He nodded slowly. "You're finally beginning to understand, Perris. That's how I operate. If I don't reach out and grab what I want, there's no one who's going to hand it to me."

He wasn't smiling, and she felt that tiny chill again. He sat back, making no move toward her, but the cool scrutiny of his glance raked across her skin like a rough hand. Perris felt her mouth go dry. If he said he wanted her, that she was one of the things he planned to reach out and grab, she would have to go. She couldn't stay on those terms, knowing what the stakes were.

But he didn't say it. Almost as though he knew what the consequences would be, he held back. Still, the knowledge that it was a possibility quivered between them for a long moment.

"Am I going to get my wind-surfing lesson?" she asked at last.

"Is that what you really want?" he responded, one eyebrow raised.

Of course it was what she wanted. What else could she have come for? Unfortunately, she knew the answer to that only too well.

"Yes," she told him firmly. "That's what I really want."

He removed the sailboard and carried it up through the shallow water to the shore, where he could more easily put together the mast and rig the board. She followed him, listening all the while to his running lecture on how she was to go about sailing the small craft.

"Okay, get aboard." He held the flat hull steady while she stepped gingerly onto it, staying in a crouch and weaving as she tried to keep her balance despite the unaccustomed instability beneath her feet. It was like trying to keep control of a surfboard. She'd never tried surfing, but she began to have a healthy respect for those who did it well.

She looked down at the colorful sail lying in the water before her. It was attached to the hull with a hinge. How was she ever going to keep her balance long enough to get it upright?

"Take hold of the up-haul line," Robert told her calmly, pointing out the rope she was to use, "and stand up, at the same time pulling the sail up with you."

Perris steeled herself and tried, but she ended up

landing headfirst in the water with an undignified splash. She came up sputtering, furious at the laughter in Robert's eyes.

"Hey, take it easy," he told her, laughing at her incoherent protests. "Everyone falls at first. It takes time to teach your mind and your muscles to move in unfamiliar ways."

Reluctantly, she tried again. At first, it seemed hopeless, but eventually she began to get a feel for what was required, and when she actually took off on a sail of a few feet, the thrill she felt was beyond anything she'd known before.

"Wow, it's like flying!" she told Robert as he pulled her out of the water once again. "I've got to try that one more time."

He laughed, but shook his head. "It takes a lot of strength to wind surf, and I can see that you're getting tired," he told her. "Save it for another time."

She wanted to argue. After all, not only was she beginning to enjoy it; she was apprehensive about what was to come after the wind surfing was finished. She had to go back. Yet she didn't want to.

"How did I do?" she asked, then bit her tongue at the coyness of her question.

"Pretty well." He gazed at her levelly, not about to give away any flattery.

She felt a flash of annoyance at his reticence, and it prompted her to probe a little more. "As well as Janey?"

He was trying to keep from smiling, but the laughter gleamed in his eyes. "You can't compare what you did with what Janey did."

"Oh?" she said stiffly. "Why not?"

"Because you were trying to wind surf. Janey had a very different goal."

She hid her smile behind a curtain of hair as she walked back toward the catamaran, splashing through the shallow water. At least he wasn't fooled by the sort of game Janey played. That was something, wasn't it?

She helped Robert pack the board away and lash it to the catamaran. Neither of them spoke except when necessary. She wondered if he was dreading the end of their time together as much as she was.

"Time to get back to the others, I guess." Her voice sounded almost plaintive, and she avoided his eyes. "It must be nearly two o'clock by now."

"It's not that late." But he vaulted up onto the trampoline alongside her and began to pull the boat toward the float.

Was this it, then? Were they just going to sail back across the bay? A lump of disappointment filled her throat, no matter how she chastised herself for being so unrealistic. This had been a magic moment away from reality. It was time she got back. She had no business being here.

She noticed that Robert wasn't untying the rope that held them to the float as she'd expected. Instead, he was pulling something in.

"What are you doing? Pulling up your weight rock?" she asked, leaning over his shoulder to see what he was up to.

"Not exactly."

Then she saw that the rope he was reeling in was not the main one that held the float in place but a second rope, and suddenly a large black case tied to the end of it burst out of the water.

"What's that? Pirate treasure?" she asked, intrigued.

"Something like that," he agreed, unlocking the case and breaking it open. Inside was a foil-wrapped bottle of champagne lying between two crystal glasses. "I always keep a little refreshment on ice in case of emergencies," he explained.

She laughed softly and leaned back against the rigging while he popped the cork and poured the sparkling gold liquid into her glass.

There was something exquisitely ridiculous in this scene, she decided. Here they were, the two of them, water dripping from their hair, dressed in only the thinnest of bathing attire, feet dangling in the green water of the lake. And yet they were preparing to drink champagne. She grinned, liking the incongruity of it.

"What shall we drink to?" she asked when she had her glass in hand.

"Freedom," he answered without hesitation.

"Freedom?" Somehow that took the edge off the fun for her. "What sort of freedom?"

His teeth flashed in a wide grin. "Your freedom."

He touched his glass to hers before she had a chance to draw it away.

Perris hesitated, glass still extended. She ought to wipe out that toast with a strong protest. He meant her freedom from her engagement to Stan, and that was something she couldn't drink to. She ought to refuse. But the glint in his eyes told her that it was what he was waiting for, and for some reason, she couldn't stand to give him the satisfaction of knowing her so well. Besides, she didn't have to view it as a hope to rid herself of Stan.

"I have freedom," she said lightly instead, pulling her legs out of the water and stretching them straight in front of her before taking a quick sip of the cool, tingling wine. "I do exactly what I want."

"Like hell you do," he growled, dropping down to lie on his side, his head propped up on one elbow, only inches from where her legs were stretched. "If you did exactly what you wanted, you'd tell Stan to get lost, and you'd come with me."

He was crazy. She wanted no such thing. "Oh, really?" She tried for an icy tone, and for once she felt that she'd succeeded pretty nicely. "And what makes you so sure you're what I want?"

His grin was slow and lazy, and he set his glass down so that he could reach out and take her slim ankle between his thumb and forefinger, holding it loosely, like a toy. "I can feel it, Perris," he said huskily. "I can feel the way your pulse quickens when I touch you."

She stared down at his hold on her ankle, knowing he was right. Just the sight of him, eyes narrowed against the sun, drops of water still lying like tiny diamonds on his brown skin, made her ache for something she didn't dare put a name to. It frightened her, yet attracted her at the same time. She knew it was wrong, but she couldn't seem to stop it.

His fingers released her, but his flattened hand began to draw a gentle circular pattern on the inside of her ankle. She bit her lip, wanting to tell him to stop but unwilling to let him think that the movement of his hand on her sensitive instep bothered her.

But it did. Just the soft touch of his calloused hand sent shivers high up her leg. She had to tell him to stop.

He spoke again, watching her reaction as though confident of his reception. "There are other bits of evidence, too. I can hear the quiver in your voice whenever you feel the pull between us."

Her breath was coming so quickly now that she was afraid to say anything for fear of giving him just the evidence he claimed to notice. His hand was moving higher, tracing a design across her calf, and she felt her leg stretch toward him of its own accord, foot arching, muscle contracting. His fingers were gentle, yet they sent a current of fire racing through her veins. Why was she allowing this? Why couldn't she stop it?

She knew she should pull away, but she looked out over the water instead, pretending it wasn't happening. As his hand moved higher, lightly massaging the inside of her knee, she knew that she couldn't pretend for long. She resisted the temptation to close her eyes and let her senses carry her away. That was something a hedonist would do, someone with no values, no ideals. Standards had always been very important to her. Why was she having such a hard time remembering them now?

"But there's more," he went on softly. "What convinces me most of all is the question I can see haunting your eyes."

"What question?" she asked with careful calm. Maybe if she pretended that this wasn't happening, it would all fade away, and they would go back to being two friendly people drinking champagne on a catamaran in the hot desert sun.

"Oh, no." He shook his head. "You're going to have to ask it. I won't do it for you."

She had no idea what he was talking about, but she knew that it was all part of the assault he was launching on her senses. She gasped as his hand moved higher, tickling the tiny hairs on the inside of her tan thigh, sending a wave of convulsive sensation up her body.

"I don't have any questions for you," she said breathlessly. "Not that kind, anyway."

She tried to move away, but his fingers tightened against her flesh, stroking in wider and wider circles. "What kind, Perris?" he teased. "What kind are you talking about?"

The fingers of his other hand were suddenly on her breast, seeking the hard kernel of her nipple through the thin fabric of her suit. The raw flash of desire that swept through her left her shaken as she'd never been before.

She twisted away from him in one explosive movement, turning so that she was lying flat, stomach down on the trampoline, upper body supported by her elbows. "Stop it, Robert," she warned shakily. "We're not going to do any of that this time."

5

❧❧❧❧❧❧❧❧❧

Perris expected Robert to contradict her, to follow her and take her in his arms, forcing a struggle she wasn't sure she had the strength to win, so when he merely laughed softly and lay where he was, watching her with his penetrating eyes, she had to admit, to herself at least, that she was a bit disappointed.

His provocative touches had roused something in her that threatened to take her over if she let it. The prospect was infinitely tempting, but the result could be disastrous, and she knew it. She wasn't one to let herself get caught in potential disasters. She was much too careful for that. Why had she agreed to go with him at all?

"You spilled your champagne," he pointed out, and she looked down at the glass lying on its side, its contents flowing away. Guiltily, she righted the glass again.

"Does that cancel out the toast?" she asked him.

"Do you want it to?" he shot back.

Did she? She wasn't sure what she wanted. No, that wasn't quite true. She knew exactly what she wanted. But she wasn't willing to pay the inevitable price. She wasn't willing to hurt Stan, either. And that would be exactly what she would be doing.

"Here." With his free hand, he lifted the bottle and poured fresh champagne into her glass. "We can make a new toast if you prefer."

She shook her head. "I think we've done enough toasting," she muttered. "I shouldn't be here at all."

He took a long, slow drink, watching her over the rim of his glass. "That's where you're wrong. You belong here. You shouldn't be anywhere else."

She looked at him candidly. "Where do you belong, Robert Chase? Why are you here? Where did you come from?"

His eyes darkened as though she were treading on forbidden ground. "I thought you didn't have any questions."

No questions? What a laugh. It was her turn to smile. "I lied. I have a ream of them."

He stared back at her. "What if I don't have the right answers?"

There was a thread of meaning in his tone that she took quite seriously. She knew that his answers would be totally different from hers and from those of her friends. If he brought those differences out in the open, maybe she would be able to see how wrong he was for her. "Then it would be best to know that right from the beginning, don't you think?"

Suddenly, he was laughing again. "Beginnings, middles, ends—can't you go beyond that, Perris? Can't you take life as it's offered, without shoving it all into categories?"

"No." She sipped her drink, then turned back to him.

"No, I can't. I'm a responsible person, Robert. I have people depending on me. I could never let them down." There. She was lecturing herself as much as anyone.

"Stan?" he asked, his voice touched with scorn.

She nodded. "Stan, yes. But mostly my mother. She needs me right now, and I have to be there for her."

He frowned curiously. "You seem to have an unusually strong attachment to your mother."

Did she? She only wished that she'd realized it earlier if she did. All those years she'd hardly written, rarely phoned. She had to make up for that now. Looking out over the water, she ran her tongue over her lips. "My father died recently, and she hasn't recovered from that yet."

His voice was skeptical. "It really hit her that hard?"

Hadn't he ever known a married couple who were in love? "Of course. They'd been married for almost thirty years. She doesn't know how to go on without him."

He was quiet for a long time. She watched the wind tossing the water of the lake into ragged whitecaps. A high cloud bank was coming in from the desert, pushed along by a hot summer wind. The skiing wouldn't be much good anymore. She ought to get back.

Robert's low voice returned her attention to their conversation. "My mother and father fought every day of their marriage. When they finally separated, the neighbors gave a block party to celebrate."

Perris shifted, turning on her side to face him. "That's too bad. They must have loved each other once."

"Did they?" His mouth twisted sardonically. "What makes you think that?"

She frowned at him. "They must have been in love when they married."

He shrugged. "If they were, marriage certainly killed the emotion."

A sudden realization came to her with painful certainty. "You don't believe in love, do you, Robert?"

His eyes were dark and unreadable. "That's one of those questions you won't like the answer to. Why ask it?"

He didn't believe in love. That was why he could discount her feelings for Stan, even her allegiance to her mother. How could she deal with a man who knew nothing of real tenderness?

She turned to look at the tiny sails in the distance, bobbing like multicolored corks on the blue water. She and Robert were very far away from everyone, hidden in their own little haven. Chase Haven, he'd called it.

She felt his hand settle on the small of her back, and she knew he was moving closer. It was time to make her move, if she was going to make it at all.

He didn't believe in love. But why did that cut so deeply? After all, there she was, supposedly in love with Stan but allowing herself to be captivated by another man. Did she love Stan? Did she love anyone?

His hand was tracing the line of her spine. He'd come up next to her, and she could feel the warmth of his breath on her shoulder. She closed her eyes and knew that the fire would soon start again unless she did something to stop it.

"You worry too much, Perris," he said softly. "Take it as it comes."

Slowly, she turned back and found his face only inches from hers. "I can't do that," she protested. "I shouldn't be here."

His hand was massaging her, slowly slipping the swim-suit straps from her shoulders, then gliding back down her spine to burrow into the small of her back. She did nothing to stop him, though she knew she should. Why was it so impossible to resist him? She'd never had trouble resisting masculine advances before.

She'd always been the one in control. This time, he was making all the decisions.

"Then don't be here, Perris," he whispered against her skin. "This isn't you; this isn't Perris Fleming. This is a mermaid I pulled in out of the deep." He chuckled as his lips grazed her shoulder. "Be my mermaid."

She had to smile in spite of herself. Wouldn't it be fun to be able to do that? To be able to submerge herself in a game of pretend? Then she could forget the rules he wanted her to toss to the wind, forget them for just long enough.

"My long, wet mermaid." His hand was rimming the edge of her swim suit, just over the end of her spine; then a finger slipped beneath the cloth and opened the way for a full caress.

"Mermaids don't live in lakes," she said softly, not protesting the impudence of his exploration, though her mind cringed from her own audacity. "They live in the ocean."

"Is that right?" He was nibbling on the back of her neck, and she leaned her head forward, letting her hair fall down in front of her shoulders. He moved in, sending exquisite chills flowing freely through her. "Then what are you?"

The warmth of his breath on her neck, the touch of his tongue, the light firmness of his hand as it slid softly under her swim suit and cupped her bottom, the low resonance of his voice, all combined to render her speechless. Her eyelids grew heavy, her movements lethargic. At the same time, a wild energy was running through her blood. The two disparate impulses formed a strange counterpoint that fascinated her. She couldn't pull away, though she knew she ought to. She wanted to stay, though she knew she should go.

"What do you call a beautiful water creature with hair

like dark fire and skin that glows like the inside of an oyster's shell?"

His words were punctuated by tiny, gentle nips along the center of her back, and she writhed under his touch, breathing faster.

"Are you going to tell me that I also have a long, scaly tail that flaps around on the deck?" she managed breathlessly.

"Oh, no." His laugh was a low rumble against her skin, and his hand took full possession of the area it was massaging. "Nothing so inelegant."

Bravely, she half rolled over and threw back her head, then looked into his face. "Are mermaids elegant?" she asked, looking into the depths of blue eyes that seemed as infinite as a starry night.

"Very elegant," he replied huskily. His lips touched hers so softly that she could barely feel the caress. "They swim like ballet dancers." He kissed her again, and then his free hand was sliding across her chest, freeing her from her swim suit and cupping one naked breast. "They make love," he whispered, "like angels."

He was going to make love to her if she let him. Right there under the sun. That knowledge fired her blood until it sang in her ears, and she knew that she wanted him to do just that.

"Who do they make love with?" she whispered back, turning to let him have all of her body. His hands pulled down her suit until it was clinging to her hips; then his tongue barely touched one taut nipple.

"Every mermaid must make love with the man who catches her," he stated flatly. "It's the unwritten law of the sea."

She felt wonderfully warm and lazy, yet excited, too. She was beyond rational thought now. He had cast a spell, and she had no recourse to logic. Stan had faded from her memory. She and Robert were in a strange and timeless place, living a dream that had no connection with the rest of the world. She wanted him in a way that she'd never wanted any other man. She felt a part of him, a part of the natural setting around them. How could that be wrong?

She loved the way he teased her, the way he called her a mermaid. She giggled softly. "You keep forgetting that this is a lake."

He stopped and gave her a mock glare. "You're putting a real damper on this seduction in case you hadn't noticed."

"Am I?" She was on her back now, and she reached up to thread her fingers through his thick blond hair as he came down on top of her. "If your technique gets thrown off course so easily, maybe you ought to think up a new line."

"I don't want to waste time thinking up lines," he rasped into her ear, and his hips came down on hers, making her gasp at the thrilling evidence of the fullness of his desire. "The only thing I want right now is you."

His body was so hard, so strong, that she wanted to feel it touching her everywhere, to feel it move against her, and she lowered her arms to wrap them around his back, holding him to her as tightly as she could. She felt the euphoria approaching, the point from which there would be no turning back, when all the world would be blocked from their minds and only this, the love the two of them were creating, would be real.

But she knew that it was impossible. Little by little, reality filtered back through the dreamlike mist he was creating around them. She had to stop him. If she didn't do it now, she knew, deep inside, that she would always feel the shame of what she'd done. She began to push, trying to dislodge him; at the same time, a new sound came to her ears, and she stiffened, recognizing it immediately. It was the high whine of Gary's jet boat.

"Stan's back," she said softly, lying very still beneath Robert.

"Forget Stan," he growled into the hollow of her neck. "You don't have to go back there."

But she did have to go back there, and not only for Stan. Her mother was involved, too. Robert would never understand.

"Stop, Robert." She propped her hands against his shoulders and pushed firmly, finally finding the strength she needed. "We can't. Not here. Not now."

His shaggy blond head rose, and he looked down into her eyes. What he saw there must have convinced him that there was no point in arguing, because he rolled off her and sat back, watching, legs crossed in front of him, while she rose and began pulling on her suit.

She knew he was angry. Why shouldn't he be? She should never have let him think that there was any chance they might make love.

Yet, to her chagrin, there had been a chance. A very good one. If the sound of the jet boat roaring back into the bay hadn't come just when it had, they might already have been in the midst of man's ultimate union. The thought raised goose flesh all across her skin despite the hot summer wind blowing across the lake. She hardly dared think about how close she had come to doing something so awful. What she'd almost done was nothing short of betrayal.

She'd always despised those modern types who lived every day as though it were going to be their last, who thought only of their own pleasures, disregarding the feelings of others if they got in the way. She'd always admired those Victorian and Edwardian novels in which the hero and heroine controlled their passions because to fulfill them would hurt others whom they loved. And here she'd been ready to throw every value she cherished to the winds for the touch of a stranger. She felt almost ill.

Finally, Robert spoke, his voice low and gravelly. "If not here, where? If not now, when?"

She was on the point of saying nowhere, never, but she made the mistake of looking into his eyes before the words were out of her mouth. Once she'd done that, she couldn't say them.

"Don't expect anything like that," she muttered evasively, wishing that his crystal gaze weren't quite so hypnotic. "I have to get back," she reminded him.

He nodded slowly and leaned over to begin untying the rope that held them to the float. Perris sat down on the canvas as Robert set the sails and let the wind start them on their trip across the bay.

The wind was stronger now, and as Robert leaned out over the spray, providing ballast for the sleek catamaran, Perris had to turn her head to keep from staring at the beautiful physical picture he made, muscles taut, body arched out over the water, with the wind flattening his hair against his head.

Instead of watching him, she looked toward their destination. Soon she could make out the canopy, then the red boat tied near the shore. As the people began to take form, Robert came over near her.

"You've still got time to change your mind."

She tried to smile. "Haven't you had enough of this mermaid?" she asked lightly. "Aren't you secretly a little glad to throw her back into the water?"

"Oh, no." To her relief, he laughed. "The man doesn't throw the mermaid back until he's made love to her. And you haven't let that happen yet."

Her heart skipped; then she turned away. She must

never let that happen. She must never be alone with him again. That might be the only way to prevent it.

They were too close to shore for her to comment. She waved at her friends, then saw Stan detach himself from the others and come down to meet their arrival. She had no idea what he was going to say, and at that point, she didn't really care much. Her concern was all with Robert, at the way she was leaving him. Her heart ached with longings she knew she had to suppress.

"Hi," she called to Stan with false cheer. She jumped from the cat and waded through the shallow water toward him.

"Where've you been?" His voice told of his outrage, but as she looked into his eyes, she saw the hurt there, too, and suddenly she was very ashamed of having put it there.

"Robert took me for a sailboarding lesson." She tried to make light of it, hoping he would follow suit. "The wind was better across the bay, so we went over there. How was your trip upriver?"

But Stan wasn't looking at her anymore. His eyes were on Robert, who was just coming onto the shore, and the gleam in them was menacing. Gary and Greg came sauntering down to stand behind Stan, looking like wary reinforcements. Perris looked at them nervously, at the three of them standing together in masculine defiance, at Robert facing them, his carriage easy and casual, but also ready and alert. If there was a fight because of what she'd done . . . If Robert should be hurt . . . Her throat was suddenly very dry.

"I thought I told you to stay away from Perris," Stan said evenly.

Robert smiled, but she could read the steel behind his grin. His shrug was deceptively lazy. "I'll stay away from her when she tells me to."

Stan made a gesture toward Perris. "Tell him, Perris. Tell him you don't want to see him again."

She hesitated, looking at Stan. She'd hurt him, and it wasn't fair of her. He'd done nothing to deserve the treatment she was dishing out. She had to make amends. Besides, she had to get Robert out of there before this confrontation boiled over into something ugly.

Forcing herself, she turned to face Robert, carefully avoiding meeting his gaze. "I don't want to see you again, Robert," she said firmly. "Stan's right. I've been foolish."

She risked a quick glance at his face. Robert looked as though he didn't quite believe her, but she could see that he was angry that she'd sided with the others. Stan came up beside her and put an arm around her shoulders, drawing her close. Robert's eyes narrowed as he looked at Stan's arm against her skin. Something seemed to twitch along his jaw line.

"I guess that toast was canceled out when you turned over your glass," he said softly.

For just a moment, she wasn't sure what he meant, but then she remembered his toast, when he'd wished her freedom. She'd argued then that she *was* free, but maybe he had been right, after all.

"I can't live with your kind of freedom," she answered, though her heart seemed to crack at the effort. "Please go."

His eyes darkened threateningly, and though his lips were still smiling, she knew that something hard and dangerous had come into his mood. "Are you sure that's what you want?" he asked harshly.

She nodded, hiding the misery she felt.

He stared at her for a long moment, then shrugged. "Okay, Perris," he said softly. "I guess this time the mermaid throws the man back."

Without waiting for an answer, he strode down to his catamaran and prepared to sail away. Perris turned with Stan and the others and walked toward the canopy, not daring to look back.

Perris never got her run up the river, but she hardly noticed. The rest of the afternoon passed in a blur. Everyone tactfully ignored what had been played out before them, trying instead to recapture the fun they'd always had so many years ago. But for Perris the effort fell flat. She couldn't get Robert's hard, angry look out of her mind.

When she asked Stan to excuse her from the date they'd planned for that evening, he didn't argue. He knew as well as she did that the bloom had gone off the event for the time being. She was grateful that he didn't force her to discuss Robert, but she wondered how he could drop the subject so easily, pretending that nothing had happened.

The next morning, he phoned to say that he'd been called back to Los Angeles for a few days. She offered to drive him out to the airstrip, and he took her up on it. But when they were alone together in the car, she found that they had little to say to each other.

"Check up on the place for me now and then while I'm gone, will you?" he asked her almost formally. "I'm always afraid I forgot to turn off a hall light or something."

"Of course I will." She was waiting for him to extract a promise from her not to see Robert while he was gone. What was she going to say when he did? She'd resolved during a long, sleepless night that she would give him that promise, that she would stay away from the other man. It was the only logical thing to do. But waiting for Stan to bring the issue up was nerve-racking.

He handed her his key, then leaned over to kiss her.

"I didn't want to leave you alone like this, especially now," he said gruffly. "But my father insists. There's a stock-option threat pending, and he wants me in on the action."

He really was a dear. She wanted so badly to feel the sort of attraction for him that she felt for Robert, but she knew that it just wasn't there. She wanted to reach out, to take him in her arms and tell him that everything was going to be fine, but she wasn't sure it really would be. Instead, she just smiled. "I'll be all right."

He hesitated. "I hope so," he said doubtfully. Throwing her a half smile, he took up his suitcase and started toward the private plane that was to take him back to L.A. and his father's company. "Be good."

And that was all. Perris watched him climb the ramp, watched the Cessna taxi down the runway, then take off into the clear blue sky. Be good. He hadn't asked her to promise anything. Could she trust herself to stay away from Robert without having made that promise?

As it turned out, she really didn't have all that much choice in the matter. Though she spent most of her time entertaining her mother with card games and books from the local library, she did find a few hours each afternoon to spend out on the beach or walking along the shore, where she knew that Robert could find her easily if he wanted to. But he never did.

She saw him now and then, but only from a distance. Once, when she was on the beach, she saw his catamaran far out across the lake. She stood and shaded her eyes, but it didn't come near.

Another time, she saw him driving by in his little green sports car. She was walking on the sidewalk, and he must have seen her, but he didn't slow down.

Well, fine, she told herself. It's just as well. The man is no good for you, Perris. Be glad that he finally realizes it, too. You should be able to breathe easier, Perris, old girl. Get ready for your wedding.

In a fit of determination, she went out and raided the bookstores for every bridal magazine in print. She took them all home and spread them out across her bed, then sat back and stared at them, unable to open a one.

Instead, she got out her violin and played the saddest gypsy songs in her repertoire, until her mother finally climbed the stairs herself to ask her what was wrong.

"Not a thing," she said, an artificial smile plastered on her face as she put her instrument back in its case and snapped it closed. "Just thinking, that's all."

Her mother reached out a blue-veined hand to touch the rough surface of the black case. "Something is bothering you, Perris," she insisted with something close to her old spirit. "If it's the music . . . if you want to go back to studying . . ."

"Oh, Mother." Perris gave her mother a bear hug and laughed. "That's over. No more dreams of that sort. I think I'll look into joining a local orchestra when we get back to Beverly Hills. Some group that plays once a week just for the joy of it. But that's as far as it will ever go again."

She knew that that was true, and for once the realization didn't sting. Something else had taken the place of that disappointment, something that seemed to cut just as deeply into her heart.

But that was ridiculous. What was she thinking of? Her heart had nothing to do with what she felt for Robert. There, she'd actually admitted that she felt something. Now maybe she could deal with it. What she felt for Robert was pure physical lust. Wasn't it?

But some terrified place deep within her soul told her that it just might be more.

Her mother's condition was very much on her mind. Perris knew that the only answer to her mother's readjustment lay in reintegrating her into an active life, giving her a new focus. She'd heard about adult classes that were being offered at the local community center and wondered if her mother might be interested in some of them, but when she asked friends what they thought, she got a mostly negative response.

"Oh, don't force the poor thing to go down there" was the usual reply. "Bring her out to the country club. Let her sit in the sun and watch the tennis."

But sitting around watching life go by was not what Perris had in mind for her mother. One day in the middle of the week, she took her on a driving tour of the town, pointing out how Lake Havasu City was growing and stopping, as if spontaneously, to take a look around the community center.

Her mother balked at first, not even wanting to get out of the car, but Perris pressed her until she grudgingly conceded.

"Oh, all right, just one little walk. Just to that fountain in the courtyard. Then let me sit and rest."

Perris had stacked the deck, gaining the cooperation of some of the volunteers who staffed the center ahead of time, and soon a parade of people were coming through the courtyard, each showing off a painting or a piece of sculpture he had just made. The friendly atmosphere and the intriguing work being done got to her mother, just as Perris had hoped they would, and by the time they were driving back home, she'd convinced her mother to try a few classes herself.

"I'll need help, you know," she warned her daughter. "I can't get around on my own."

Perris smiled happily, thoroughly relieved at this sign that there was going to be a light at the end of the tunnel.

But though there was hope of improvement on her

mother's side, her own case was less encouraging. Time after time, she found herself sitting by the window, looking out at the lake, lost in memories of a man's voice and touch that were only a few days old.

It was because of those same memories that she lay awake a few nights later, staring at the silver beams of moonlight that found their way through her window. She'd turned the air conditioner off and opened a window at nightfall, depending on the usual cool of the desert evenings to keep the temperature down. But the wind off the Mojave was hot that night, and by midnight the air was stifling.

She got up and leaned on her window sill, peering out into the shadowy darkness. The green belt below looked spooky in the gray light. She could imagine all sorts of scary things hiding among the trees. But then her mind went back to the morning when she'd met Robert there, and suddenly the area seemed warm and inviting again. She looked toward the end of the development, but the Castlemeyer house wasn't visible from her room.

A vague sense of restlessness was eating away at her. She couldn't play her music now for fear of waking her mother. The only other remedy she could think of was a walk along the waterfront.

Leaving on her short cotton night shift, she slipped into her light robe, belted it at the waist and tiptoed down the stairs. After opening the front door, she lifted her face to the hot breath of the wind and stepped out into it.

The fronds of the many desert palms rustled crisply as she passed, and the wind whipped her hair across her face. She made her way down through the parking lot, across the bridge, and out onto the beach. The sand felt almost as hot on her bare feet as it had under the daylight sun many hours before. She stared out at the tiny lights blinking at her from across the inky dark water. Was there no one else awake but her? Slowly, almost as though she couldn't help herself, she turned and looked up the beach to the Castlemeyer house.

The huge structure rose like a Gothic mansion against the night sky. There was a light burning in a downstairs room.

Numbly, she turned and walked back across the bridge. It took her only moments to make her way up the street to the big house. Her footsteps slowed as she neared it.

The light was coming from what seemed to be an attached garage. She stopped on the sidewalk, but though she could see something moving through the window, she couldn't quite make out what it was. To see better, she would have to go closer.

She didn't even stop to think it over. Luckily, the front yard was planted with a carpet of grass, and her feet made no sound as she walked through the hedge and along the side of the driveway until she came to the low window. There was no curtain, and inside the well-lit garage, she saw the shell of a sailing boat. Robert's blond head was bent over a workbench, and he was sanding a long piece of wood with a hand sander.

The night was hot, and as usual, his clothing consisted of the absolute minimum. He wore only a light pair of faded shorts, and his torso was bare. A patina of sweat shimmered in the lamplight across the tanned flesh of his back, outlining the slope of each muscle as he worked. She watched as he sanded vigorously, then more slowly. Finally, he reached out to run his flattened hand gently down the length of the board, testing it.

The dull ache that she'd been living with turned raw

at the sight of him. She wanted to call to him, make him acknowledge her presence. But she knew she couldn't do that. She had to leave, and quickly. How embarrassing it would be to be found there, looking at him through a window.

But she couldn't leave quite yet. For another long moment, she watched as he walked over to the boat he was building and laid the newly sanded piece of wood where it was meant to go, frowning with concentration as he fitted it in place. She had to move forward in order to keep him in view, and as she did, she brushed against the side of the house. His head came up at the sound, but he wasn't looking at the window, and she ducked back, breathing hard.

This was ridiculous. If he caught her there, she'd die! Quickly, and as silently as she could, she slipped back to the sidewalk and ran for home.

Her heart was beating so fast that she was afraid to lie down on her bed, so she spent the next ten minutes pacing her room, forcing herself to calm down.

What was wrong with her? Was she going insane? Was she going to let a mad obsession with this man ruin her life? Ruin the hopes of all those who loved her? She had to stop it, and right now. Biting her lips so hard that she knew she must be drawing blood, she made a promise to herself. No more Robert Chase. She was going to forget him. It was over.

To her surprise, she fell asleep as soon as her head hit the pillow. But she dreamed about a Viking ship with a blond sailor at the helm.

The next morning, Perris was relieved of the burden of thinking much about what she'd done because Kathy called and invited her out for lunch. Melody was coming, too, and they all met at a little French restaurant that had a panoramic view of the lake and the stark black mountains behind it. Hanging plants and wicker baskets filled with croissants gave the room a festive air, and Perris was glad she'd accepted Kathy's invitation once they'd met and found a table.

They ordered strawberry daiquiris and sat back to watch the sailboats scudding across the lake, chatting about the old days and filling in some of the blank spaces of the last few years. Perris was having a pleasant time, but something about the way Melody kept smiling at her, her little round cheeks puffed out like a chipmunk's, didn't quite ring true. She smiled back, but a tiny wriggling suspicion began to surface.

"Was there some special reason why you two asked me along today?" she said bluntly, picking at her spinach salad.

The shadow of guilt that swept across both faces told her that she'd hit a vein of truth.

"We just wanted to see you, Perris," Kathy assured her hurriedly. "You're an old friend."

"Stan called you, didn't he?" She knew she'd guessed right as soon as the words were out of her mouth. "What did he say? 'Keep an eye on Perris for me.'"

"Oh, no, Perris. It was nothing like that," Melody blurted out. "He only wants us to help ease you back into the old gang, that's all. He's afraid you don't feel like one of us anymore, and he asked Kathy and me to be sure you get involved in our activities . . . sort of reintroduce you."

Perris laughed. She was partly touched by his concern, partly resentful. "What are you two planning? Another coming-out party for me? A sort of post-debutante ball?"

"Oh, no, Perris. What an idea." They both laughed.

"But listen," Kathy went on kindly. "Melody and I

are in charge of planning the country club dinner dance for the Sundance Regatta two weeks from Saturday. We haven't come up with a good theme yet, and we were thinking . . ." She hesitated and looked to Melody for support.

"What would you think of turning the dance into a Romance Rendezvous? That'll be the theme, and announcing your engagement will be the highlight of the evening," Melody said in a rush. "Stan thinks it's great. I have the cutest idea for centerpieces made with red hearts and this gorgeous white lace. Oh, say we can do it, Perris!"

Luckily, the entrée arrived at that moment, and Perris was saved from having to show her real reaction to the plan. Pure terror was shivering through her, and she had to take a quick drink of water to clear the panic from her throat. As the waitress placed their meals before them, she chastised herself internally.

Grow up, Perris. You told Stan you would marry him. A week ago, you were perfectly happy with the idea. Nothing has really changed. Face reality. Stop trying to hide away in dreams.

Of course she would say yes. What else could she do? Marrying Stan would make everyone happy. It was what she wanted, too. She couldn't hang back now and pretend to need more time to think things through. She had to step up and meet her future. She'd vowed to wipe Robert Chase from her mind, and she was prepared to do just that. Once her heart had settled down, everything would be back to normal.

"It sounds wonderful," she told them when the waitress had left. "I can't wait to see your plans."

The relief the two of them felt was evident, and Perris wondered just how obvious her recent doubts had been. How seriously had they regarded her ride across the bay with Robert? She was resolved to forget all about it herself.

They were talking and laughing, and she'd almost reached a point where she felt like a real part of the group when she looked up and saw Robert entering the restaurant. Everything else fell away as she stared at him. All she saw was the radiance of his light hair, the glow of his crystal-blue eyes. He was dressed in an open-necked blue shirt and brushed denim pants, and she thought that he'd never looked more attractive. His gaze locked with hers, and he came toward her. It wasn't until he reached the table that she realized that he had a woman on his arm.

"Hello, Perris." His smile took in all the members of her party, but his gaze quickly came back to meet hers. "How've you been?"

"Fine, thanks," she said stiffly, holding back the clash of emotions that was spinning through her.

"I'd like you to meet Talia." His teeth flashed against his tan as he grinned down at the blonde who was clinging to his arm as though she hoped to keep it forever. "Talia is a friend from out of my past. She stopped by to see me on her way to New York."

Talia had the carefully cultivated look of a voluptuous Hollywood starlet, and she had little time to waste on a tableful of women. Her heavily mascaraed eyelashes barely flickered in recognition of the introductions Perris proceeded to make, and then her attention was all on Robert again.

"Will you be staying in Lake Havasu for long?" Perris asked, then bit her tongue, wishing she hadn't been quite so blatant about her interest in the length of Talia's visit.

"Just for a few more hours," Robert answered. "Talia

has a part in a musical that's opening on Broadway next fall. She has to get back to rehearse."

"Come on, honey," Talia said, her impatience showing. "Let's find a table and eat. I want to get a good meal in you." She winked back at the others. "He needs his energy for a long good-bye."

Perris stared out at the lake as Robert and Talia walked away to a table at the other side of the room. She hoped the other two couldn't see any evidence of the storm that was raging through her. What was it exactly? Anger? Indignation? Hatred? Pain? She wasn't sure herself. But she had to keep control.

"He's been taking Janey out lately, you know," Melody said, an "I'm only telling you this for your own good" look on her face. "She says he's crazy about her."

"Oh, Perris." Kathy reached out and covered Perris's hand with her own. "Men like that are nothing but trouble."

Perris wanted to say that Robert meant nothing to her, that she couldn't care less who he was dating, but the words stuck in her throat, and all she could manage was a defiant smile.

"Listen, I was crazy about a fellow like that in my senior year of college," Melody told them both. "He was captain of the football team, tall and gorgeous." Her eyes misted over with memories. "He had a way of holding me so tight. . . ." She sighed, then shook the memories away. "Anyway, when I took him home to meet my parents one weekend, I could see immediately that he would never fit in. I mean, he called my father, 'hey, man,' all the time and cracked his knuckles at the dinner table. Really. We broke up first thing Monday morning, and I started going with Greg, and"—she shrugged happily—"life has been perfect ever since."

Was life going to be perfect once Perris put her feelings for Robert behind her and threw herself into planning an engagement party? Somehow she doubted it.

The rest of the lunch seemed to last forever. As she listened to Kathy and Melody talk about parties she hadn't been to and the care and feeding of young children, she knew that something inside was rebelling again.

She wanted a family. She wanted a husband who loved her, a house and children. But did she want that quite yet? Was she really ready? Something in the panicked feeling that filled her when she thought about it told her that she probably wasn't.

But what else was there? What did she really want to do? Go with Robert? What would happen if she did?

I'll get up, she fantasized silently, pretending to listen to the other two talk, and I'll walk over to Robert's table. I'll twist my mouth into a sophisticated sneer calculated to strike terror into Talia's cold little heart. I'll say, "If you want me, Robert Chase, all you have to do is whistle."

She just managed to hold back a secret, rueful grin when she realized how slim the chances were that he would respond by taking her in his arms and raining mad, passionate kisses all up and down her neck. More likely, his answer would be a casual "Get in line, Perris. Janey and Talia got here first."

When Perris and her friends rose to leave, she steeled herself to keep from looking toward Robert's table, but she felt his presence, anyway. She barely managed to remember to say good-bye to the others before turning to get into her car. Somehow she had to rid her mind of the man.

Her mother was due at the community center at three, and Perris was surprised to find her already dressed and waiting when she got home.

"You're starting to like it, aren't you?" Perris asked her almost accusingly.

Her mother's smile was grudging. "It does fill up the day," she admitted.

"What's on tap for this afternoon?" Perris asked as she settled her mother into the car.

"I'm going to try the literary discussion group."

"That makes the third activity you've tried," Perris noted approvingly. "Along with the art class and the woodworking." She frowned. "I must say, I've had my doubts about that last class. Won't it require a lot of physical effort?"

Her mother smiled back at her. "Not the way I take it. I only go in to watch the others. The instructor is very good, and I love to see the beautiful wood creations everyone comes up with."

Perris pulled into a parking space in front of the entrance. "Now, you remember, if you get tired or don't feel well, tell one of the volunteers to call me."

"I will, dear." The older woman allowed her daughter to help her out of the car and into the building, where one of the ladies who volunteered to help the less able members get around was waiting. "You go on and let me have my own fun."

Perris watched her mother being led off and turned back to her car. It was working just as she'd hoped. Her mother was looking brighter every day. Would she be recovered enough to accept it when Perris and Stan broke up?

When? Now where had that come from? she asked herself guiltily. How about *if?* Anyway, the issue didn't

hinge only on her mother's physical strength. It also
involved the guilt Perris felt for those years in Vienna,
the overwhelming determination she now had to make
everything up to her mother in any way she could.
Perris knew she couldn't get out of her predicament that
easily.

6

⊶⊶⊶⊶⊶⊶⊶⊶⊶⊶

That night was just as hot as the previous one had been, but for some reason, Perris still couldn't bear to leave the air conditioner on. She wanted her window open; she wanted to watch the breeze fill her curtains. It was almost as though she thought that closing her window would lock something out, something that she very much wanted to welcome in.

She lay on her bed for a long time, and finally she realized she wasn't going to fall asleep. She wasn't even trying to. She was waiting.

Waiting for what? She rolled over and buried her face in her pillow. What did she think? she asked herself scathingly. Did she really believe he was going to come climbing in her window? What was the matter with her?

She turned again and stared up at the ceiling for a long time. Who was she trying to kid? Telling herself that she was going to forget Robert was like telling herself that she was going to stop breathing for a while. It just wouldn't work.

She knew what she had to do, and she knew she would do it. But if she did, she also had to admit that her relationship with Stan was over. If she went to watch Robert again, she couldn't pretend to be in love with Stan, and if she didn't love him, she couldn't marry him. It was as simple as that.

Could she break Stan's heart and destroy all her mother's hopes just for a passion that consumed her? There wasn't really a choice any longer. Perhaps she wasn't as strong as the people in Victorian novels who turned their backs on love to pursue goodness instead. She knew she wasn't strong enough to fight what she was feeling now.

Finally, she rose, put on her filmy yellow robe and walked down the stairs, just as she had done the night before. This time she didn't go down to the shore first. Instead, she turned directly toward the Castlemeyer house.

The light was on in the garage again. She stopped at the edge of the sidewalk, trying to calm the loud thudding of her heart, but she had no thought of turning back.

The night was deep as purple velvet strewn with diamond stars. A hush filled the area. She could smell the scent of orange blossoms faintly now and then. The grass was cool on her bare feet. The hot wind caught at her robe and sent it billowing around her. She pulled it back and went on toward the window.

The newly made shell of the boat was there, just as it had been before. The workbench had a fresh layer of sawdust. But she saw no sign of Robert. Where was he? She couldn't stand to think of not seeing him. She pressed up closer to the glass, trying to see into every corner of the stark, unfinished room, searching every shadow.

"Lose something?"

Robert's voice came from directly behind her, and she whirled, hand to her mouth in horror. How could he have come up behind her without her hearing a thing? The desert wind gusting through the night must have masked his footsteps. What had he thought at finding her there? How could she explain her presence at his window?

His hair looked like spun gold in the moonlight, but his eyes were as hard as sapphires. He wore only a brief pair of shorts and torn tennis shoes. His muscular body gleamed like bronze in the light from the window, reminding her of a statue of an athlete from some ancient age. She wanted him as she'd never wanted anything else in her life.

His gaze held hers for a long moment that hung suspended between them. She couldn't read his expression, couldn't see what it was that he planned to do. But she knew what lay before her. There was only a dark and menacing road, and she knew that she had to tread it.

Slowly, she lifted her hand and turned it toward him, palm up, as if in supplication. Something moved in his face. She couldn't have said what it was exactly, but she knew what it meant. Suddenly, she was moving toward him, rushing into his arms, and he was pulling her in against his naked chest, holding her so tightly that she could scarcely breathe.

"Robert . . ." she gasped. "Oh, Robert, I . . ."

"Hush." He buried his face in her auburn hair. "Don't try to explain. I feel the same way. God knows I've tried to get you out of my mind all week."

She lifted her head to look at him, glorying in his

nearness, in the lines of his handsome face, in the tenderness of his desire. Then she was hungrily seeking his mouth, and he took her to him, his lips moving on hers, seeking to draw something from her that she didn't know how to give. But she would give him all she could. Everything.

She reached higher to wrap her arms around his neck, arching her body into his, stretching against him. His hands curved around the fullness of her hips, pulling her in to feel the strength of his need for her, molding her to him as though the heat of their love would bond them forever.

A strong gust of wind tore at them, ripping at her gown, and she clung to him, her hair whipping across his face.

"Come on." His voice was hoarse, and he swooped her up in his arms as though she were made of gossamer. His front door opened easily, and he kicked it closed behind him. She lay pressed against his chest while he climbed the stairs, her eyes closed, her hair floating around her head in a cloud, listening to the drumbeat of his heart.

She was his now, in her heart and in her mind. Soon she would be his in body as well.

He placed her gently on a bed, and she opened her eyes again, reaching out to stop him when he started to move away. With a soft moan of protest, she let him know that she couldn't part with his touch even long enough for him to take his few clothes off, and he leaned over her while she pulled quickly at the belt of his shorts, releasing them so that he could kick them off along with his shoes, sliding her hands along the hard muscles of his back, the smooth shallow of his belly, the hot strength of his thighs.

His mouth taunted hers, taking slow, tormenting

kisses, then drawing back while she reached up for more.

"Robert," she whispered, half pleading, half commanding, "don't tease me. I feel as though I'm on fire. Please . . ."

He responded by taking possession of her mouth with a sweeping kiss that destroyed all rational thought. As his tongue moved aggressively, taking control and searching through her for any secrets she might be hiding, she felt herself opening to him, demanding more, showing him just how ready she was to return his ardor.

A sense of urgency flowed through her with the fire in her blood. She needed him now, right now. Twisting beneath his touch, she helped him to pull off her robe and gown, then reached up to draw him to her, and he came without hesitation.

His dark hands circled her breasts and tugged at the nipples, raising them until they were high and sensitive. Leaning down, he stroked each darkened peak with his tongue, rasping gently against them until she writhed with desire. As the trembling began in her legs, she reached to touch him, to run her palms over his hard chest, digging her fingers in gently when a spasm of ecstasy shook her. His mouth was like molten heat on her skin, and his tongue began to explore every hidden secret she possessed, while she moaned and reached for him, impatient to have all of what he had to offer.

She hadn't given him time to turn a light on in the room, but she hardly noticed. Her world was contained in the tiny space their two bodies occupied and nothing more.

He was breathing fast and deep in his chest, and the sound of it excited her even more. Without any urging, she prepared to receive him, coaxing him on with tiny whimpers when he didn't seem to move quickly enough to suit her, crying out in triumph when the union was complete, losing herself in the oblivion of mutual desire brought to the pinnacle of fulfillment.

His hands on her skin conjured up magic. The sounds from his throat, the beating of his heart, the warmth of his breath on her neck, sent her reeling. His body pressing on hers brought her to a state of near frenzy. She heard a growl and realized dimly that it was her own.

Together, they rode the steep slope of the wave they'd created between them, higher and higher, like an endless ride on a mystic sailboard, catching a wind that left them breathless, then cast them high into the air, only to crash back into the wave as it broke against the shore, leaving them spent and lifeless.

They both lay where the wave had left them, slowly regaining their breath, holding tightly to one another as if they could hold on to the moment, make it stay.

Of course, that was impossible. Perris could feel it slipping through her hands like silver sand even before her breathing became even again. But still she held him, held him as though she would never let him go.

She loved him so. She'd never known love could be like this, so raw and demanding, then so soft and tender. She'd never known she could generate the sort of passion he'd displayed or harness it once it ran wild. But she'd done it. They'd done it. If only it could last forever.

She closed her eyes. Freedom. He lived for it. Could he ever give it up for her? Could he ever include her future in his?

She would never marry Stan. Of course, she wouldn't. Not when she knew she loved Robert this way. But would Robert ever compromise his dreams? Did she dare to hope?

He was raising himself above her, looking down into her sleepy face. "Thank God that's over," he said with relish.

Her eyes flew open, and she stared up at him. "What exactly do you mean by that?" she asked in bewilderment.

His smile was slow and lazy. "I didn't think I was going to survive. I've wanted you so badly for so long—I thought I'd go out of my head."

She put both hands on his shoulders. "Not used to waiting a week, are you?" she said, a bit of sarcasm spicing her words.

He shook his head. "I'm not used to wanting one woman so completely," he said softly, as though it surprised him as much as he had meant it to surprise her.

She watched as he slid off her to lie by her side, his head propped up on one hand. Every curve and angle of his body was fascinating to her. She was unembarrassed now and could put out a finger to follow the line of his neck or reach to curl the hair around his navel with no feelings of hesitation. He was hers, at least for the moment, in a way that superseded everything else.

"You knew it had to happen, didn't you?" he went on. "I knew it, too." He touched her hair and smiled. "You tried to deny it, especially when you let Stan make you send me away the other day. But I knew you couldn't fight your destiny."

She laughed, catching hold of his hand and pulling it to her lips for a quick kiss. "My destiny? How very pompous you sound."

"Um hmm," he murmured. "Unlike me, isn't it? But I caught you, my beautiful mermaid, and I had to make love to you. I told you it was the law of the sea."

She closed her eyes, enjoying the caress of his hand in the valley between her breasts. "Are you going to throw me back now?" she asked, half fearing the answer.

"Not on your life," he said huskily, nipping at the lobe of her ear. "I'm amending that part of the law. The man makes love to the mermaid every hour on the hour for the rest of eternity. How's that?" he asked, well pleased with his idea.

She laughed again. "You have a wonderfully optimistic view of your own stamina, don't you?" It felt so nice to be able to talk to him this way again. Their banter came easily. He felt right for her. Did he see it the way she did?

"Are you kidding?" he was saying. "We'll eat seaweed in between. It works every time."

She turned to smile into his face. "It might work for mermaids, but I can't see how it would help humans much."

He took a handful of her hair and let it sift through his fingers. She watched the way the moonlight played across his face; then he looked into her eyes, frowning with intensity. "When I saw you in that restaurant today, I wanted to grab you right there. You looked so beautiful with the sunlight streaming in around you, lighting your hair with golden fire. I wanted to walk through the room, throwing aside tables and chairs, leaving screaming people in my wake, and pick you up, throw you over my shoulder and walk out."

"What stopped you?" she asked, bemused. She remembered her own fantasy of that afternoon.

He shrugged. "Stupidity. The next time, I'll go ahead and do it."

She wondered what sort of next time he had in mind. Should she tell him that she'd decided to break off with Stan? But he must know that. What she'd done that night had shown him. She didn't have to put it into words.

"You are sort of a dog in the manger, aren't you?" she asked dreamily.

His hand stopped moving on her skin. "What do you mean by that?"

"Well, I heard you were seeing a lot of Janey. The way they're telling it, you're crazy about her." She opened one eye to see his reaction.

He chuckled, resuming the slow massage. "Janey is . . . How can I put this? Janey is there when you need her. She's even there when you don't need her. Janey is a good sport."

Perris wasn't sure she liked that description of the woman she'd once called her friend, though she couldn't call her that right then. Maybe the next day.

"How did you know I was going to be outside your window tonight?" she asked, stretching luxuriously against him. "Were you out there waiting?"

He laughed softly as he stroked the length of her, touching her softly as though she were made of velvet and silk. "I saw you disappearing down the sidewalk last night. I went after you. I stood out in the green belt and watched your bedroom for an hour after your light went out."

She sighed, enjoying his caresses, enjoying the play of light and darkness across his skin, enjoying the warm summer night. "You should have climbed up the side of the house and come in the window. It was open." What would she have done if he had? She thought she knew. The immediate combustion between them would have flared, just as it had that night.

He was nuzzling the hollow behind her ear, sending tiny chills along her spine. "Would you have welcomed me then?" he whispered.

Her laugh was low and throaty. "I would have devoured you. Can't you tell?"

He was quiet for a moment; then he began to let his

tongue explore the curve of her ear. "I couldn't do that, though," he murmured. "You had to come to me."

She turned to look at him. "And I did, didn't I?" She felt no shame for what she'd done. As he'd said, it was destiny. The moment they'd met, they'd both known it was inevitable.

"You did," he agreed.

"What would you have done if I hadn't? If I'd stayed in my house and never come out?"

He chuckled. "If you'd kept that up for long, I would've had so much practice climbing the walls around here, I'd have had no problem climbing up to your bedroom."

He'd wanted her as badly as she'd wanted him. The knowledge warmed her but didn't provide a lot of comfort. After all, he was a man who didn't believe in love, and she was a woman with promises to keep. What they had together was something special, something apart from the rest of life.

Perris looked around at the dusky room. Even in the dark she could make out the African masks and woven baskets displayed on the walls. Somehow they didn't seem to reflect what she knew of Robert's taste.

"What are those things you have on your walls?" she asked.

"They aren't my walls," he replied lightly.

She looked at him. "Isn't this your bedroom?"

He grinned. "No. I don't think I've ever been in this room before. My bedroom's at the back of the house. I just threw you onto the first available bed I came to."

Her mouth opened, but there didn't seem to be anything to say. They both began laughing, and he wrapped her in his arms again, rocking her gently.

His shoulders were so wide, and the rich, male scent of him filled her. She breathed it deeply into her lungs, closing her eyes and glorying in his warmth.

"Tell me who you are, Robert Chase," she said softly. "Tell me why you're here in Mrs. Castlemeyer's house. Tell me what you want out of life."

His hand was stroking her hair. "Right now all I want, all I can think about, is you."

She smiled. His hair was tickling her nose, and she rubbed it against his chest. He knew how to say the right things. She wished she knew how much of what he said he really meant.

Probably not a lot. He was a man who knew how to make a woman happy. Her mind shifted back to Talia, she of the curvaceous body and long good-byes.

"Were you thinking about me when you were with your friend this afternoon?" she asked, then winced, for her voice sounded more malicious than she'd meant it to.

"This afternoon?" He had the nerve to act for a moment as though he didn't know what she was talking about. "Oh, you mean Talia, don't you?"

"Yes. What were you doing there? I mean, it was kind of a coincidence, being in the same restaurant."

He chuckled. "This time I wasn't following you, though," he admitted. "This time it was pure luck."

"Yes, what luck," she answered, a bit of a sting in her tone. "What luck to get to see you with that sexpot."

He tipped her face back so that he could see her expression. "Were you jealous?"

She refused to give him the satisfaction of admitting it. "Should I have been?" she asked instead.

Suddenly, his eyes lit with laughter. "No, I won't make it easy for you," he told her. "I want you jealous. I want you to turn into a wildcat whenever another woman comes near me."

She narrowed her dark eyes and flexed her nails against the skin of his chest. "Be careful, Robert," she warned, only half joking. "Wildcats tend to scratch anyone who crosses them. Even their masters."

"Then I'll have to treat you very gingerly." He reached down slowly and took her lips between his own. "Would you like a sample of how careful I can be?" he whispered against her mouth.

He was ready to begin the wild magic between them again. She was tempted to stay and let him. But she couldn't.

"Robert, I must go home."

He stiffened for a moment, and she thought he was going to argue, but then he relaxed again and dropped less serious kisses on her mouth.

"That word 'must' again," he growled. "I'm going to have to find a way to wipe that word from your mind."

Slowly, she removed her arms and legs from between his own and sat down on the bottom of the bed to begin dressing. He lay back against the pillows and watched her.

"What sort of boat are you building in the garage?" she asked.

She loved the slow grin that crept across his face. "I knew it. You're really a spy, aren't you? You've seduced me in order to get the plans to my boat."

She pouted, then rolled her eyes. "You know my secret. How can I go back to my brutal spy master and tell him that I've failed?"

He rolled off the bed and pulled her up after him. "I'll reveal all to you, my darling," he said dramatically, clutching her to his chest. "Your love is worth far more than my plans could ever be." He grinned down at her. "Come on. I'll show it to you."

Her protests were shrugged aside. "It'll only take a minute. You can't go without seeing her. Next to you, she's the grandest lady in my life."

How could she refuse an invitation like that? She waited while he put on his shorts; then he led her down the stairs and through the dark living room into the triple garage.

Stacks of wood and boxes of power tools littered the floor. In the center of the room, the boat sat, fresh and new. It looked closer to being completed than she had thought, now that she saw it clearly. She gazed at it for a moment, but boats weren't things she knew much about, and she couldn't think of anything appropriate to say.

"It looks like a lot of work" was all she managed; then she frowned, for she could see by the look on his face that he'd expected more.

"Work!" The word fairly exploded from him. "Building a boat isn't work. It's a labor of love." He grabbed her arm and pulled her closer. "Come here. I'll show you."

Taking her near, making her touch each piece of wood and learn what its purpose was, he gave her a quick lesson in shipbuilding. He demonstrated how he'd first constructed a frame for the hull, then carefully attached the wood.

"I used strip planking," he told her. "Each narrow strip is fitted, glued and nailed into place on the one that went before, bending to conform to the curve of the hull. Then the framing is removed."

When the hull was completed, he'd worked on the cabin and was now finishing the teak deck.

"The railings will be mahogany," he said, holding up the pieces he'd already formed. "Just feel the grain on this. Isn't it beautiful? Here's where it will go."

He pointed out where he planned to use the rail, running his hand over the spot with such tenderness that Perris couldn't help but smile.

"This little beauty will race like a devil wind," he said lovingly, emotion shining in his face as he stood back and gazed at his creation.

Perris laughed softly. "Robert, how can you say you don't believe in love?" she asked him without thinking. "Anyone who loves anything like you do this sail-boat . . ."

Her voice faded away as she watched his eyes widen at what she'd said. For just a moment, a flame of haunted vulnerability shone there, as though she'd touched a nerve he'd thought had lost its sensitivity, surprising him. Then it was gone, and he was showing her how nice and big the cockpit was going to be.

"The cabin is primitive. Just the bare minimum, as you can see. I'll be the only one using it, and I won't need it for anything but occasional shelter, so I short-changed that area to give myself more room where I'll really need it."

They stood back and looked at the boat, and Robert reached out to put an arm around her shoulders and draw her to him.

"Where did you learn to do this?" she asked wonder-ingly. "Surely it doesn't come by instinct."

"No. I learned all about boatbuilding as a kid in Portland, Oregon. I used to hang around the shipyards, doing odd jobs to make a little money. Then, when my mother got sick, I had to quit school and get a job that paid enough to keep food on the table. I lucked into an apprenticeship with a boatbuilder. He made mostly plastic and fiberglass hulls, but on his own he built wooden boats in the old style. He taught me everything I know."

She looked at him, more interested in his past than in boatbuilding. "Did you get to go back to school? Did your mother get well?"

A veil had come over his bright eyes, and she knew

that her questions were unwelcome. After only a minor hesitation, however, he answered. "No, I never went back to high school. My mother died, and I had two little sisters to take care of."

"Oh." The word seemed very small, but she didn't know how to convey what she felt. She could feel him bristling. He didn't want sympathy. He'd rather she forgot the whole thing. But how could she? It was a part of who he was.

"How did you get this job?" she asked.

He looked surprised. "What job?"

She opened her arms expansively. "Taking care of Mrs. Castlemeyer's house."

His slow grin was back. "Another stroke of luck, I guess," he said. "Have you ever been in here before?"

She shook her head. "My mother and Mrs. Castlemeyer are friends, but I was in Vienna when they became close."

"Then you've never seen the rooms."

"No, I haven't."

He took her hand. "You've got to see the rooms."

She started to hang back. "Oh, Robert, I really have to go."

"Just a little tour," he coaxed. "Come on. You'll love it."

They started through the large house, with Robert switching on lights as they went.

"This is the living room. Pretty conventional, wouldn't you say?"

She agreed. The room was big, with low ceilings and thick carpets and furniture that was tasteful but unexciting.

"This," Robert continued, "is Mrs. Castlemeyer's public face. Her real personality is expressed in the bedrooms."

"How many are there?" Perris asked as she followed him up the stairs again.

"Eight. With six baths."

"Isn't that a bit roomy for a lady living alone?"

"Ah, but she isn't living alone. Just wait and you'll see what I mean."

The first room he opened exuded an exotic scent, and when he turned on the light, it was filtered through the gauzy colors of dozens of silk scarves that hung from the ceiling. Huge pillows were scattered about the floor, and a large, low brass table sat in the middle of the room.

"Shades of Scheherazade," Perris breathed.

"Exactly. Look at the next."

In the neighboring bedroom, the floor was covered with finely woven tatami mats. Again, low pillows were the only seating, and a lacquered table, set with an exquisite oriental floral arrangement, was the focus of interest. Along the walls, glass case after glass case displayed lovely Japanese dolls.

"Come on," he urged before she could say a word in reaction. "You've seen Japan and the Middle East. Here we have a British retrospective."

The next room was the image of an English country house. The bed had a high canopy. Logs were laid in the cheery fireplace, ready for the next winter chill. Comfortable rockers and armchairs were set about it.

"Every room is a different country," Perris exclaimed.

Robert nodded. "Mr. Castlemeyer was an officer in the Foreign Service. They spent most of their marriage in countries all over the world. After he died, Mrs. Castlemeyer built this house, partly to store all the things they'd collected over the years and partly to store her memories. Look at this."

He took her into the room and showed her a shelf

along one wall that contained framed pictures, picture albums, scrapbooks and other mementos.

"Every room has a shelf like this. A history of the years she spent in that country. She kept journals all that time." He pointed out a cloth-covered book. "Whenever she comes, she stays in whichever country she feels like remembering. She can see pictures of all her friends from those days, read over her journal, hold the very objects she used in that country."

Perris was enchanted. "What a fascinating lady she must be. Most people only dream of bringing their past experiences to life again. She's gone ahead and done it." She shook her head in admiration. "Are there more?"

There were more. One room recreated a Dutch kitchen, another a Swiss chalet. Peru came to life with llama-skin rugs and Indian blankets and wall hangings.

"And you've seen East Africa," he reminded her.

She met his smile. "Which room do you sleep in?" she asked. "Or do you travel from one room to the next like she does?"

"Oh, no," he replied. "They're not my memories. I feel a little guilty about intruding in Africa, if you want to know the truth." He turned her toward the back of the house. "I sleep in here."

This room was smaller than the others. A small single bed covered with a royal blue spread and a desk and chair were the only furnishings. The walls were covered with blueprints for sailing vessels and pictures of sailboats surging through rough seas.

"Very nautical," she commented.

"Of course," he replied. "But you should see my bathroom."

He led her through his room to a door on the other side. There she found a huge bathroom made entirely of marble, from the old-fashioned stand-up sink to the very new fashioned marble shower that opened up into a Roman tub.

"You couldn't very well fit something like this onto your boat, could you?" she said, reaching out to touch the smooth, cold surface of the walls.

"No," he agreed. "But when I'm sailing, the sea is my bathtub." He curled an arm around her shoulders. "That reminds me," he said lightly. "Mermaids can't stay out of the water too long. It's about time we did something about that."

She looked at him uncertainly. "What are you planning now?" she asked, trying to edge away from his arm.

"Only a quick shower." He grinned as his free hand came up and captured her chin. "Come on, mermaid. You know you've been out of the water longer than you should."

She couldn't help but laugh back at him. "I don't have time for a shower. . . ."

But even as she spoke, he was beginning to pull her robe from her, and she felt too pleasantly lethargic to stop him.

"We have all the time in the world, mermaid," he said huskily as he slid the silky cloth of her night dress from her body, watching it fall away from her full breasts and slip down over the swell of her hips. "All the time in the world."

She recognized the flame that sprang to life in his eyes. She felt it, too. Reaching out, she helped him remove his clothes, as well. "One quick shower," she whispered to remind him, and they moved toward the huge shower area.

Robert turned on the spray, and they stepped into the marbled interior. "First I soap you," he told her firmly. "Then you return the favor."

She looked at him and nodded in mock deference while he positioned himself under the water and put her outside the faucet. Tonight she would play his games. She wanted to be with him, to know all about him. Tomorrow—well, it was best not to think of that.

The bar of soap he used had a minty smell, and he lathered his hands generously before he began spreading it across her shoulders.

"Remind you of the sea, little mermaid?" he murmured. "Can't you just smell those refreshing sea breezes?"

She chuckled softly. "No, but I can feel that salty nip in the air. I'm standing out here freezing while you get all the warm water."

"You're not going to freeze," he promised her, his soap-slickened hands cupping her breasts to begin clothing them in the white suds. "I'll make sure you stay very warm."

She sighed and leaned back, eyes half closed, letting him coat her with tiny bubbles. He was right; the coolness was gone, for his hands, moving across her, roused the fire in her soul. She gasped when he touched a particularly sensitive spot, and he murmured something low and touched it again.

"Oh, Robert . . ."

"Turn around."

His hands felt like a warm wind caressing the lines of her back, coating her with the marvelous substance that made movement so easy. She closed her eyes and abandoned herself to the sensations.

She heard the bar of soap hit the marble floor and felt his arms slide around her, pulling her in under the stinging water, slipping her along the length of his body, and when she opened her eyes, she saw the deep intent in his.

"Oh, no, you don't," she told him, leaning down to retrieve the soap. "I get my turn."

Rubbing the soap in her hands to create a slippery foam, she began to lather it across his body, giggling when she hit a ticklish spot, laughing when he complained, soaping every inch of him below the chin. "You look like the Abominable Snowman," she told him, and he lifted his arms menacingly.

"You know what the Abominable Snowman does to mermaids, don't you?" he roared, making as though to grab her, and she darted out of the shower, leaving the warm spray to him.

"I have a feeling mermaids get pushed around a lot in this world," she said from the depths of a thick yellow towel. "I wonder if they've thought of organizing an equal rights movement?"

"Not on your life," he answered, happily washing off the soap suds. "A good mermaid knows her place."

Perris lifted her head. "And where is that? Right under a good man, I suppose."

"Of course." He began to whistle as he turned beneath the warm stream of water, and she looked around for a way to express her indignation at his attitude.

Turning on the hot water in the sink as hard as she could so as to draw it away from the line to the shower, she called in to him cheerily, "Cold enough for you?"

She was rewarded by his yell as his nice warm water turned to the temperature of ice cubes, and dropping her towel, she ran laughing from the room.

She didn't stop in his bedroom. He was coming right behind her, water flying from him in all directions. She turned out into the hall and ran for the stairs. He caught her on the landing.

"You're going to pay for this act of defiance, little

mermaid," he threatened, snagging her and tossing her down beside him on the plush carpeting. He held her hands to the floor and leaned down over her vulnerable body. "You're going to pay . . ." He kissed her soundly. "And pay . . ." His voice was husky as he lowered his body over hers. "And pay . . ."

The love they made was slow and delicious, and she never wanted it to end. His hands could make her feel like a being from another dimension, able to move through space and time in ways she never had before. The effect of the thrust of his masculinity was like being hurtled high in the vortex of a cyclone. He was the hot wind of summer, and she was his to carry with him where he willed.

When the storm died down and left them both gasping for air, clutching one another, holding on to the feeling, she felt a sliver of fear enter her thoughts.

She felt things for this man that she'd never felt for Stan. She'd known that from the beginning. At one time, she'd thought it was just lovemaking that she craved from him. She'd considered the idea that fulfilling that need might possibly make her able to forget him. Lying there in his arms, she knew that it was not to be. The more she had of him, the more she wanted. This was even more than what she'd thought it was. This was a passion that challenged everything she lived for.

"Robert," she said suddenly, dashing the disturbing emotions from her mind, "we left the water on! The bathroom will be flooded!"

He flopped back away from her as though too exhausted to get up. "Get the mops," he ordered wearily. "Women's work. I'll just wait here while you . . ."

Laughing, she rose over him threateningly. "Listen,

swabby, it's a sailor's job to clear the decks. And it's your bathroom. I could walk right out of this house and leave you to do it all by yourself."

"Never should've given them the vote," he muttered, forcing himself up, and the two of them went off, arm in arm, to see how disastrous the damage was.

7

~~~~~~~~~~~~~~

Perris lived the next few days in a haze of unreality. She spent her mornings with her mother, then drove her to the community center for the afternoon. While her mother was gone, she walked the beach, played her music or caught up on her sleep. Then she picked her mother up, joined her for dinner and tucked her in bed. As soon as she was sure that her mother was asleep, she slipped out of the house to join Robert.

She knew that she had to let Stan know how things had changed. She was ready to do that if only he would return. But she dreaded it at the same time. Once she'd done that, she'd have to tell her mother. How was she going to break it to her?

Robert wasn't usually free during the day. She assumed that it was because he was working on his boat, and that worked out well for her because she needed to spend the days with her mother. But she thought about him every minute. There were times when she wondered what life had been like before he'd come to bring her his vitality.

They couldn't stay apart. It was as though there were some mystical, hypnotic force pulling them together. And when they were together, they had to touch each other every moment. She couldn't hear his voice without reaching to feel his warmth, and he couldn't see her without caressing her cheek.

Yet they both knew that it was a relationship on the edge of a precipice. They both knew that Stan would be back soon and that things would come to a head when he returned. What would happen to their idyll then? Neither of them had yet spoken the question aloud, but it haunted the dark shadows of the night when the lovemaking was over and pearly-pink shafts of light crept into the sky, heralding dawn. Each time Perris prepared to slip home before her mother awoke, they both knew Stan might return that day.

They did have one morning together. Perris's mother went to visit a friend, leaving Perris alone, and she invited Robert over for breakfast, squeezing him some of the blood orange juice from the oranges that she'd shown him before.

Anxious to make use of the sunshine, they drove to the London Bridge to play tourist for the morning. Perris led Robert through the Trafalgar Maze, losing him among the oleanders, then finding him again along the row of little pubs made to look like something out of jolly old England.

"This English village was built by the city of London," Perris told Robert. But he had eyes only for the bridge.

"The London Bridge in the middle of the Mojave Desert," he said wonderingly. "It boggles the mind, doesn't it?"

She shrugged. "Not when you're used to it. Come along and see the other shops."

They browsed through the shell and jewelry stands, admired the pen-and-ink drawings being exhibited and bought some fudge at the candy store, but their favorite was a unique candle shop that sold wax sculpture and had relics of the British Empire on display.

"Queen Elizabeth's carriage in a candle shop." Robert shook his head. "You're sure we haven't gone through some sort of looking glass, aren't you?"

They took a cruise around Thompson's Bay and got a look at the bridge from the other side.

"Still just as big," Robert commented dryly.

"The bridge was taken apart, piece by piece, shipped to Long Beach, trucked to Lake Havasu and put back together like a giant jigsaw puzzle," the tour guide told them.

"It does add a touch of class to the neighborhood, wouldn't you say?" Robert asked the woman, but received only a puzzled look in reply.

Robert's favorite place in the village was an amazing shooting gallery peopled with animated mannequins— men, geese, frogs and other assorted creatures—that darted up and down, played the piano or honked or croaked when hit by the beam of light sent out by a rifle. Once he'd tired of setting them off himself, he fed quarters to all the children who were hanging around the place, waiting for their parents to come out of the candle shop.

Perris watched as he treated every child with calm, humorous dignity. He's going to make a wonderful father, she thought to herself, then pushed the traitorous idea away.

They went through the maze one more time, had a pasty and went home.

One night halfway through the week, she was helping

him caulk joints on his creation late into the night. When he worked, he became totally absorbed in what he was doing, but he was always aware of her presence, as though she were somehow a part of his effort rather than a spectator.

"Why are you doing this?" she asked him all at once. "Why not just go out and buy a boat and use all this time sailing it instead of working on it?"

He swung around to face her as though she'd just asked whether he thought the world was flat, after all. "Sometimes I forget what a landlubber you are," he sighed. He took the caulking gun from her hand and drew her away from the boat.

"Come on. We need a break. How about a glass of wine? I've got a nice bottle of Chardonnay in the refrigerator."

She followed him to the kitchen, cleaned her hands in the sink and then went with him out to the living room, where they sat down on the long couch. Robert was wearing a powder-blue cotton shirt and, as usual, faded cutoffs. Having known that she was going to be put to work that night, Perris had dressed in forest-green shorts and a green and red plaid shirt.

"Let me explain something to you," Robert began. "Every sailboat is an individual, just as people are. Each boat has its own personality, its own way of approaching a challenge. When I decided to make a trip around the world by sailboat, I knew I'd have to build my own boat, a craft carefully planned to do exactly what I wanted it to do."

"Trip around the world?" she echoed, not sure if she was more appalled or intrigued by the idea. "I thought you just wanted to sail around the lake."

"No, darling." He reached out with one hand and took up a lock of her auburn hair, twisting it absently around his forefinger. "This is an oceangoing beast I'm creating here. A tough little number that'll be able to withstand heavy seas and long stretches without maintenance."

Perris knew very little about ocean sailing, but she did know that it was dangerous. "That little boat in the middle of the ocean?" She wrinkled her nose in distress. "How are you going to get it there?"

"It's a simple matter by boat trailer."

"You could get killed out there, couldn't you?" That was a thought that was almost too painful to contemplate. Why would anyone take such a risk?

His blue eyes were searching her face, penetrating the depths of her gaze, as though he were trying to find something hiding there, to bring it out in the light.

"Don't you sense the challenge in it, Perris?" he asked. "Can't you imagine climbing the back of a ten-foot wave, fighting the wind and coming through in spite of it all?"

She shook her head emphatically. The man was definitely certifiable. "No," she announced with spirit. "That's not challenge; that's insanity." She frowned, unable to understand his motives. "What makes you think you can come through, anyway? What if the wave and the wind are the winners?"

His large hand curled around her neck, and he drew her closer. "That's just it, don't you see? If I can beat them, if I can tame the wind and the sea"—he wore the grin of a swashbuckler—"then I can do anything." He was smoothing her hair back, watching its dark red highlights dance in the lamplight. He shrugged, a little defensive. "Is it so crazy to want to prove myself?"

"Maybe not, if it's in a field you have some control over." Like walking, or wind surfing on a nice calm lake, she thought.

He looked surprised. "You really don't know a lot about me, do you, Perris?"

Was that her fault? He was the one who would never answer questions with anything other than a dismissive wisecrack. "Tell me, then," she urged. "Explain it to me."

"Sailing is a field where I do have control," he obliged. "I've sailed all over in all kinds of conditions. I was seventeen when I first crewed on a sixty-five-foot yacht going to Tahiti. I've been all around the Pacific since then, sometimes crewing, sometimes alone."

That made her feel a bit more secure about his safety. But she still didn't want to think of him out in the middle of the ocean, so far from her, so far from any port. How long did it take people to sail around the world, anyway? Didn't things like that go on for years?

"But why?" she asked, certain that she'd never understand no matter what answer he gave.

His hand left her hair, and his index finger began a slow trip down her hairline, around her ear, under her chin. "It's always been a dream at the back of my mind," he told her musingly. "I never really thought I would have the time to pull it off. I was always working so hard, always trying. . . ."

He shook the thought away, and her heart ached for him, wondering what it was he'd tried so hard at. Had he failed? Somehow she couldn't picture him failing at anything. Though he obviously hadn't done well in life monetarily, she'd always assumed that it was more because he didn't care than because he couldn't cut it. Now she wondered.

"Anyway, one day I took a look at my life, and I didn't much like what I saw. I decided to make a radical change. To do something that would make me grow, feel good about myself."

"So you took this job as caretaker for Mrs. Castlemeyer and began working on your boat." It would be the perfect job, she supposed. Plenty of time to do what he wanted, and money enough to live on. What more could he want? Why didn't he just stay there and enjoy it?

His grin had an odd slant, as though she'd said something amusing. "That's right," he said softly. "I needed time to complete my project. And the wind patterns on the lake are good for experimenting. That's why I use the sailboard and the catamaran. I take them out during various wind conditions to put into practice some theories of my own." He shrugged, his voice taking on a resonant quality. "That's why I came here. And it's turned out to be the best move I ever made."

His fingers were brushing lightly at the pulse point along her collarbone, then descending slowly, making small designs on her skin. "Little did I know the challenge that would confront me right here," he whispered, his fingers deftly plucking open the top button of her plaid blouse.

He smiled at his own handiwork as he admired how provocative he'd made her look with her blouse open, allowing the full swell of her breasts to show generously.

"Hardly a challenge," she said, sighing. "More like a ripple than a wave." How long would he stay with such dull fare as herself if he hungered for danger? She didn't want to think about that.

She leaned back against the pillows at the end of the couch and watched from beneath her dark eyelashes as he deliberately set out to arouse her nipples through the stiff cloth of her blouse. His fingers searched out each peak, teasing with a quick rasp of his thumb until it began to tighten, pulling high and hard against the fabric.

"You're a wave, Perris," he disagreed huskily. "You're the most thrilling wave I've ever ridden. I'll never conquer you. But I'll never stop trying."

Did he really feel that way about her? She wished she

could believe it. She moaned as his teeth closed around one nipple, biting gently through the cloth.

She wanted to tell him just how vanquished she was, but she didn't dare. If he knew, he might draw away from her, afraid that she expected things he wasn't ready to give.

"Come with me, Perris," he said suddenly, his arms wrapping around her, his body so hard and smooth. "Sail out there with me in that cold gray ocean. I need you with me."

Now she knew he was crazy. She pulled back and stared up at him. He was serious. She could see it in the flat earnestness of his eyes. "I can't," she answered automatically.

A spasm of annoyance flashed across his handsome face. "When are you going to let the wind fill your sails, Perris?" he asked. "When are you going to rush out and find what life has to offer you?"

He was acting as though she were a homebody who'd never been farther than the mailbox, someone who always did exactly what was expected of her. She'd told him all about Vienna and her music and the rebellion involved in going after that dream. Why didn't he see that she'd been doing just that, rushing out to meet life, when she'd gone through all the turmoil over her choice of career goals?

"I've done that sort of thing," she told him a bit stiffly. "When I went to Vienna—"

"Oh, Vienna." He waved it away impatiently. "That wasn't much of a risk, was it? You had a monthly allowance from your parents. You lived in the house of your violin master, who was also a friend of a friend of your parents. You might as well have stayed home."

"But I've traveled—"

"In organized tours, staying at protected hotels in the best parts of town. Perris . . ." His laugh was rueful.

"Darling, you've been around, but you haven't lived."
He ran a hand through her hair. "I want to teach you to
live, to grab life by the throat and tell it what you want."
He frowned. "Don't you ever do that, Perris? Have you
ever even had a thought along those lines?"

What did he think her obsession with him was? Her
indignation was rising, and she turned on him suddenly,
pushing him back against his end of the couch until his
legs extended along the length of it.

"Listen, mister," she told him with pretended men-
ace while she forced his legs apart and sat on her knees
between them. "You think I don't know how to reach
out and grab what I want?"

Her fingers curled around the lapels of his shirt; then,
with one quick jerk, she sent the buttons flying. He
grinned up at her, lying back as though helpless to
defend himself, and she felt a thrill at the silliness of
what she was doing.

"You think I don't know how to meet a challenge?"
she went on, pushing aside his shirt and leaning down
over him, running her hands over the rough hair of his
chest, delighting in the rounded muscles that seemed to
expand under her touch.

She bent above him, circling his navel with her moist
tongue, licking at it, pulling away, then exploring the
ridges of his ribs with small, warm kisses. She nipped at
his flat, masculine nipples with her teeth, then let her
fingers make wandering trails along the insides of his
arms.

"You think I don't know how to get my own way?"
she demanded.

Leaning on his shoulders with her palms, she lowered
her hips onto his, grinding lightly against him, then
pulling away, then again, teasing him, meanwhile holding his gaze with her own like some female Casanova
bent on aggressive seduction. "Are you going to give

in?" she asked huskily. "Or am I going to have to take more drastic action?"

He took a deep breath and slowly shook his head. "I'm a pretty stubborn guy," he said, though his words emerged with difficulty and laughter lit his eyes. "I don't crumble that easily."

"Don't you?" Her eyes still holding his, she began to open her blouse one button at a time, until the sides hung free and the full slopes of her breasts appeared in the opening. "What do you think?" she asked provocatively, arching up over his chest, then down against him, letting her taut nipples graze his skin. "Still need more persuading?"

His breath was coming faster, and his eyelids were growing heavy, but he managed to nod his head one more time. She grinned and arched back far enough that she could reach for the opening of his shorts. "Okay, mister," she said with a mock sneer, lowering the zipper with exquisite slowness. "You've had it now."

But Robert had finally gone over the edge. With a low growl, he reached for her, tearing aside her blouse so he could take her breast against his lips, arching out of his pants while tugging her free of hers.

They made love with laughter and cries of the most intense desire, and as they lay back on the floor, where they had fallen in their passion, Perris wondered how she could ever let this man walk out of her life. She loved him more than ever. Every day, every minute, only intensified her feelings for him. When was she going to have the courage to tell him so? And, more to the immediate point, when was she going to tell Stan?

Her mother's trips to the community center were doing her a world of good, but there were still bad spells when she seemed to need to cling to her daughter for support. Those incidents worried Perris, for she knew just how shaky a prop she made.

What bothered her more, though, was the new game her mother was playing—the "when you and Stan are married" game, which she lapsed into more and more often.

"When you and Stan are married," she said one day, gazing mistily out the window, "I'll come over and do your gardening for you. I'm sure you'll have some sort of job and won't have time."

She smiled happily until she saw the look on her daughter's face. "Oh, not the heavy work, but the little things, like putting in the bedding plants and keeping up your potted geraniums."

"Mother," Perris answered, "I don't have any potted geraniums. I don't even have a garden."

"But you will," the older woman said calmly. "Stan's told me about the sort of house he wants for the two of you. He's even said he would make sure there was an extra bedroom for visits from his mother-in-law."

She would have to tell her mother soon. It was cruel to let her weave dreams that had no substance. And yet how could she shatter all her hopes? Couldn't her mother sense that something was wrong? Perris looked at her apprehensively but couldn't read anything in her pale eyes other than her happiness at the plans she was making in her head.

"And when the babies begin to come . . ."

Babies and potted geraniums. Was that what Perris wanted? Of course. But not with Stan.

Yet a future with Robert didn't hold much promise of that sort of happiness for her or for her mother. What was she doing? Where was she going?

No matter how many recriminations she hurled at herself, she knew she couldn't have done anything differently. After all, how would she like being married to a man she didn't love, making him as miserable as she was making herself? Wouldn't she rather be climbing the edge of a wind-driven wave with Robert's arms around her? Just the thought of it made her heart beat a little faster.

Robert seemed to have begun to believe that she was really coming with him. "We don't have to make one forced-march trip around the world," he told her, lying among the pillows of his narrow bed and holding her head to his chest. "Somehow that doesn't seem so important anymore. But I want to take you to the South Pacific. You won't believe the beauty of some of those islands, the stunning approaches as we come sailing in. You're going to love it."

She smiled and snuggled closer to him, pretending. But inside she knew the truth. Stan had to be told. And then her mother. She knew that reality was closing in.

It came on Saturday afternoon, one week after she and Robert had begun their tumultuous affair. When she walked in from a trip to the grocery store, her arms full of bundles, her mother hit her with the news.

"Stan called while you were out."

Stan had called periodically while he'd been away. Every conversation only skimmed surfaces. He and Perris had made polite small talk about the weather, about how business was going, about what the others of their group were up to. He'd never mentioned Robert, nor had he pushed her about a wedding date.

But something in her mother's tone told her that this was different.

"What did he say?"

Her mother came into the kitchen behind her, holding back her news as though she were sure it would be received with excitement.

"He'll be back tomorrow," she said at last. "Isn't that wonderful? And he'll be back for the rest of the summer. His father has promised. No more calling him in at the last minute."

Perris set the bags down on the white tile counter. "That's great." She tried to sound hearty, and her mother apparently didn't notice how far short of it she fell.

"And guess what. He told me not to tell you, but I can't hold it back." She laughed conspiratorially. "He's got a ring with him."

Perris felt her lips turn up in a smile, but inside she was shriveling like a dry autumn leaf.

"Oh, I'm so happy!" her mother bubbled, opening the door of a cupboard and pulling out a mixing bowl. "I'm going to bake him my cherry jubilee cake, the one he always asks for. My own son-in-law." She reached over and hugged Perris spontaneously. "I'm going to think of him as my own son. I've always loved that boy. No mother could be happier."

Looking down into her mother's shining face set off an ache in Perris. How could she do anything to wipe out this joy? After all she had done before, leaving her mother to deal with her father's death alone the way she had, how could she now take away the one thing that gave her so much pleasure? And yet she knew she had to.

"Mother," she said suddenly, looking out the window at the clouds coming in over the silver-blue lake, "did you ever have doubts? Before you married Daddy?"

"Oh, no." Mrs. Fleming came up and put an arm around her daughter's waist. "Not a one. Your father came into my life and plucked me away from everything I'd grown up with. My family said he was no good, but look what he made of himself." She chuckled softly. "He was a wonderful man. I'm so glad I was able to see it even if others couldn't. We had some wonderful years together." She gave Perris a squeeze. "Just as you and Stan will."

Perris had to fight to hold back the sigh that rose in her. "What time is he arriving?" she asked.

"Ten in the morning. He asked if you would pick him up at the airstrip, and of course I said you would. Wear something gorgeous for him, dear. The poor boy deserves it after having to leave you for so long." She giggled. "Oh, and now it will be official. He'll be here for the party, so you two can announce your engagement a week from today. What wonderful timing."

Wonderful, just wonderful. Perris walked through the house and up to her room, meaning to take her violin in her arms and find some comfort from it. But when she got to her bedroom, she couldn't open the case. Her mind was full of Robert, of his strength, his humor, his thrilling ardor.

At one time, she'd thought that making love to him would cool her feelings. What a fool she'd been. Every time he touched her, he only stoked the passion she felt higher and higher and added to the strength of her love for him.

What was it women in novels always said? "I couldn't live without him." She'd always thought that was a silly phrase, but now she understood the feelings behind it.

She knew she wouldn't die if she lost him. Not really. But something inside her would shrivel and fall away. And she would never be really whole again. She loved him with every fiber of her being.

Love—that frail emotion he didn't even believe in. She believed in it. She thought she'd known what it was before. After all, there had been that artist in Vienna.

She'd planned to marry Stan. In both cases, she'd told herself that she was in love.

But now she knew the truth. What she'd felt before had been nothing compared to what she felt with Robert. He'd entered her life like a hot summer wind, blowing away her inhibitions, filling her with a new sense of her own vitality, and she would never again be free of him.

If only she knew how strong his feelings were for her. If only she could come to her mother with the hope of some relationship she could honor. Her mother would be devastated that Perris wasn't marrying Stan, but if she could look forward to another engagement, perhaps . . .

But that was crazy. Robert had made it very clear that there was nothing like that in his future. She might as well forget it.

So what could she offer her mother? If only she could think of a way to shield her from the pain.

That night, she walked more slowly than usual as she made her way under a star-studded sky to meet Robert. She didn't relish the scene before her. He was putting a coat of varnish on the hull, but when she entered the garage, he put down his brush and came to meet her.

"I've missed you," he mumbled against her hair as he held her in his arms. "The days just get longer and longer." He pulled his head back and gave her a warm smile. "Let's take the day off tomorrow. We'll take the cat and sail out to Chase Haven and . . ."

"Robert." She stopped him, shaking her head, and he seemed to notice the look on her face for the first time.

"What is it?"

"Stan's coming back tomorrow."

Just under the surface of his smile, a wall of ice

seemed to crystallize, turning his eyes as cold as the open sea. His arms loosened around her, and then they were standing, facing one another but not touching.

"So what?" he asked, his voice dangerously soft.

"I . . ." Words evaporated before they reached her lips. How could she say it? "He's bringing a ring," she managed hoarsely.

"So what?" he repeated. "There's nothing between the two of you anymore. Surely the last week we've had together has proven that."

She swallowed, avoiding his eyes. "It's not that simple." Where were the words? How could she make him see it?

"No?" His tone was harsh. He leaned back against the wall, looking down at her through narrowed eyes. "Explain all the complexities, if you please."

He wasn't making this any easier. Forcing herself to look him in the eye, she made her plea. "People are depending on me, Robert. People I've let down in the past. When I tell Stan that I'm not marrying him, a lot of people are going to be hurt."

A barely restrained rage was building behind his cold eyes. "What do you want me to tell you, Perris? To stay with Stan so only you and I will be hurt?"

She shook her head wildly. "No, of course not. But I might not be able to see you for a while. My mother . . ."

Suddenly, he lashed out and took hold of her shoulders in his strong grip. "Don't you see? You're turning your back on life again. Stan is safe and secure. He'll give you a nice house and a shiny car. Your mother will be proud to show pictures of her daughter's wedding." His grip tightened. "But what, after all, will you really have, Perris? Everyone else will be happy, but how about you?"

"No . . ." She tried to explain to him that she wasn't planning to marry Stan. She only wanted him to understand her situation. If she told herself the truth, she would have to admit that she was hoping that he would volunteer to step into the gap. But he didn't seem to catch her hints at all. Perhaps that was because he didn't really want to.

"Well, maybe Stan is the best thing for you," he was saying coldly. "You're both alike, both a pair of conformists who can't step out of the mold. Maybe you would be better off with him."

She shook her head again, trying to head him off. Only one tiny hope remained.

"Do you want me, Robert?" she asked almost desperately. "Do you want me to stay with you?"

He frowned, as though confused by the sudden turn she had taken. "You know I do. I want you with me more than I've ever wanted anything else in my life. I'm leaving to launch my boat in the Pacific in a few weeks, and I was planning to take you with me."

He did want her. She knew that that was true. But not more than anything else. He'd made it quite clear that there was nothing as important to him as his freedom.

But did he want her badly enough to make a sacrifice? The next question was the most difficult she'd ever asked. She had to pull strength from very deep within in order to mouth the words.

"Do you love me?" she whispered, her dark eyes pleading for him to say yes.

Slowly, he relaxed his grip, drawing away from her. She sensed that the distance was as emotional as it was physical. She knew the answer before he spoke.

Finally, he gave her just what she'd expected. Just what she'd dreaded. "You know how I feel about you,

Perris. It would be easy to say, 'Yes, I love you.' And I would mean it, in a way. But it wouldn't really be the same thing that you mean when you say love."

Her hands felt very cold, and she couldn't look into his glacial gaze any longer. She'd known that this would be his answer. Why had she bothered to ask?

"When you say love," he went on in a quiet voice, "you're thinking of white lace and babies and houses within commuting distance of a job." He shook his blond head. "I can't promise you that. I won't pretend I can."

He needed his freedom, the scope to move on when he felt the urge, the liberty to let the wind fill his sails and take him wherever it pleased. He might take a companion along on the ride, but there were no guarantees. She might get swept away on one of those waves he so wanted to challenge, but he would go on as before.

She looked at him and felt the lump in her throat growing into something too painful to stand. She loved him so. How could she stand to lose him?

And yet how could she hurt the others she loved for the sake of a handful of seaweed? What right had she to jeopardize their happiness? She'd been told all her life that she had to marry Stan. Maybe she needed that stability as much as Robert needed his freedom.

"I guess that answers my question," she said hollowly, starting to turn away.

"Perris." He stopped her with a hand on her arm. "Don't go. Come sailing with me tomorrow and we'll talk this out."

She shook her head, desperate to get out the door before her tears shamed her before him. "I'll be with Stan," she said huskily.

His hand withdrew as though she'd burned it. "Don't

do this," he warned. "Don't give up what we have, Perris. I want you. I need you with me. Don't go."

She couldn't speak. As she struggled blindly toward the doorway, she heard his voice harden behind her.

"Don't come back here wearing his ring, Perris. I won't take you that way."

8

~~~~~~~~~~~~~~~~~~~

Perris watched as the little plane circled the field, then settled in for a landing, its tires bouncing on the runway. In a few minutes, Stan was bounding toward her, and she managed a friendly smile of greeting.

"Perris!" He swept her into a bear hug, then gave her a quick kiss before he released her and picked up his bag again. "I'm so glad you came out to meet me. Let's get home. I can hardly wait to hit the water."

She drove him back across the London Bridge and into town, then up the hill to his parents' house. He chattered all the way, as excited as a man about to start a much-needed vacation. Did he sense the hesitation on her part? Perris knew that he must.

The home they entered had a spacious Spanish-style layout that made a U-shape around a courtyard filled with a turquoise swimming pool and green plants. A day lady and a weekly yard service kept the place in top condition even when no one was living there.

"How about a swim?" Stan suggested, pulling the knot from the tie around his neck. "You know we've got plenty of extra suits."

Slowly, she shook her head. "Stan, we have to talk."

She could see him swallowing hard, and suddenly she realized why he'd been chattering on like a magpie. He'd been afraid of this talk, and he'd hoped to avoid it. Her heart lurched with a mixture of pity and guilt. If only she'd never seen Robert on the beach that day.

"I suppose we might as well get it over with," he said, waving his hand toward the couch. "Shall we?"

He sat down nervously a bit away from her. She folded her hands in her lap, not sure how to begin.

"Well," he said at last, "let's have it. Just how far has this gone?"

"How do you know anything's happened?" she asked, then cursed herself. What a stupid thing to say. Of course he knew that something had happened.

"I could tell from the stilted telephone conversations we had every time I called you," he said quietly. "It's that Robert Chase character, isn't it?"

She cast him a bittersweet smile. "Yes."

He sighed heavily. "Do you think you're in love with him? Is that it?"

She nodded, aching for Stan, aching for herself.

"So what are your plans?" he asked impatiently. "Do you want to marry him now? What's the scenario?"

"Stan, Robert will never marry me."

He snorted in a sort of sad triumph. "I know that. He's not the type. He'll take what he can get, but he doesn't want to pay for it."

A defense of the man she loved sprang to her tongue, but she thought better of uttering it. "The point is . . . you know I love you in my own way. Not quite the way I love Robert, but in a different way, maybe a better one. I just wanted you to know . . . well, my mother is counting on our marriage so heavily. If by any chance you still want me . . ."

"Do you mean it?" A look of incredulous joy flashed across his face, and she stared at him in surprise. "You still want to marry me?"

She shrugged helplessly. "If you want me this way. I mean, I know you deserve better. . . ."

"Oh, Perris!" He slid across the couch and took her in his arms, hugging her tightly. "If I still want you! I've done nothing but want you since you wore pigtails and had Band-Aids on your knees. I was so sure I'd lost you."

She frowned slightly, thinking, That's just the case, Stan; you have lost me. Don't you get it? She'd never believed he would want her once he knew how she felt about Robert. In some ways, she had even been counting on that as a way of withdrawing from the engagement with the least amount of pain on either side. But now . . . She tried to think of how she would react if Robert told her something similar, that he really loved someone else but would marry her if she really wanted him to.

But he hadn't said that, had he? She'd been the one who'd asked him, and he'd refused her. He loved freedom best, and he wouldn't compromise that passion.

Yet there she was, ready to marry Stan, mostly to please him and her mother. What was she doing? Could she withdraw the offer?

No, it was too late. Stan was prattling on about the wedding, about the engagement party, about the life they would have together. She was really going to do this thing. Would she ever forgive herself?

"You'll forget him someday, you know," he was telling her earnestly. "This is just another of your aberrations, like going to Vienna. It'll fade away in no time."

Perris looked at him and sighed quietly to herself. Maybe he was right. After all, she'd once thought that the violin was the ruling passion of her life, and she'd become reconciled to giving up that dream. Maybe she could let Robert go in the same way.

She certainly tried to do just that over the next few days. She and Stan were together constantly, water-skiing with the gang, having a quiet dinner at Jocko's, taking her mother out for an evening drive along the lake. But everywhere she went, her coffee-colored eyes were restless, constantly searching every crowd for a certain blond head.

"Come on," Stan was always saying. "Let's try that new seafood place down by the bridge." Or the new disco in town. Or a new beach he'd heard about or a new water-skiing area. It was as though he thought fresh surroundings would keep her mind occupied.

He was so sweet. She appreciated him more, really, than she ever had before. Though he bestowed a fair amount of chaste kisses on her cool lips, he didn't push for anything more. And he included her mother in everything.

She was wearing his ring now. It was a huge marquise-cut diamond solitaire. Whenever she looked at it, she remembered how Robert had sounded when he'd warned her not to come back to him once she'd put on Stan's ring.

She was bearing up quite well, actually. Smiling came just as easily as ever. A casual observer wouldn't guess that she had a care in the world. Even the others in the old gang seemed to take the engagement at face value. Only once did the hard shell that protected her almost crack.

She'd spent the afternoon with Melody and Kathy, shopping for a dress to wear to the dinner dance on Saturday, and they'd stopped to have a cup of coffee at a little Dutch bakery.

"Where's Janey been lately?" she asked all at once, without thinking. "I haven't seen her all week."

A sudden awkward silence filled the air as her two friends looked at one another, then down at the little frosted pastries in their plates.

"Janey's unavailable these days," Melody finally hazarded. "She's been seeing a lot of that friend of yours. Robert Chase."

"Oh." What more was there to say?

It was irrational and silly and totally illogical to let that bother her, but the torture of his dating Janey tore at her for the rest of the day.

How could he so soon after what they'd had? Did it all mean so little to him?

She realized how unfair she was being, but she didn't care. It hurt, and she hated it.

In the evenings, she spent a lot of time watching the changing colors on the lake. She loved the time just after sunset when the mountains looked like black paper silhouettes against a sky the shade of a lush, ripe peach. The lake turned from silver to liquid gold, then to liquid fire, while a sliver of moon rode high above in a purple night sky that was closing like a veil over the land. She loved the scene, but it had a melancholy feeling that didn't help her peace of mind.

At night, she lay awake long into the darkest hours, wondering if he could possibly be out in the green belt, watching her room. It took every ounce of strength she had to keep from going to the window, throwing it open and scanning the greenery.

By the end of the week, she knew it wasn't working.

A marriage with Stan would be doomed from the beginning. But how was she going to get out of it?

Certainly there was nothing she could do before the party. Everyone was primed for it. The engagement had to go on. Perhaps it would be broken later, but the announcement had to be made on Saturday night.

On the evening of the party, Perris began dressing almost two hours early. She took her time, making everything perfect. After all, how many engagement parties would she ever have? Even if she had grave doubts about a wedding, this party was set in motion, and nothing could stop it now.

Though she was usually careless about makeup, for once she took her time over it, producing a face that could easily have found a place on any magazine cover. After piling her mahogany hair high atop her head, she teased down a curtain of wispy curls to dance around her hairline.

The dress she'd chosen was a jade green, finely pleated silk that left one shoulder bare and hugged her curves, only to flare out below the hips, swirling about her legs. She slipped her feet into strappy gold sandals and hung drops of carved jade from her earlobes. Then she stared at herself in her mirror.

The woman she saw there was beautiful, but she didn't recognize her. Who are you, lovely lady? she asked silently. What do you want here? Can you give me the secret to keeping everyone happy and still finding answers for myself?

But the image only stared back at her. If there were any answers hidden away behind that face, Perris knew she would have to discover them another way.

She walked down the stairs when she could hear by the sound of voices that her escort had arrived. Her mother was delighted, and Stan was virtually stunned by her appearance.

"Wow" was all he could manage at first. "Wow."

She smiled at him. "You look pretty nice yourself."

He did, too, in his black silk suit that fit his body as if it had been tailored for him.

They were taking her mother with them, but she was only going to stay for an hour or so; then Stan would drive her back home. She still didn't feel up to a full-scale party.

The three of them climbed into Stan's Mercedes for the ride up the hill to the country club. Perris felt as though she were moving in a dream from which she would awake someday, back into the real world.

The clubhouse was well lit, and the sounds of the orchestra filled the parking lot as they left the car with the valet. Once inside the building, they were swamped with friends, each wanting to say just a word of congratulations or greeting.

Perris smiled automatically and chattered back, hardly knowing what she was saying. Melody had done wonders with the decorations. White lace, usually studded with every kind of red heart imaginable, billowed everywhere.

"Isn't it fabulous?" everyone said.

The tables were set with sterling, which gleamed on the white linen. Each centerpiece was made of two red hearts formed from stuffed pillows, edged in lace and pierced by a silver arrow. Perris stared at the arrow, feeling suddenly a little faint. Then she turned back to the crowd and began circulating again.

Someone put a drink in her hand, and she sipped it. "A martini," she said, making a face. "Not my favorite, actually." But she sipped it again. She had a feeling that she was going to need all the fortification she could get.

"Hey, this is the big night," Greg announced enthusiastically as he and Melody came up to greet them.

"What do you want with liquor, Perris? You should be drunk on love."

Melody shot him a glance that had the same effect as an elbow in the ribs, and he looked around sheepishly for someone else to talk to. Stan's arm tightened around Perris. She took a deep breath and looked up at him gratefully.

It was going to be all right. She was going to make it. A special sense of her own powers of survival filled her with a feeling of pride. She would get through this evening, and then she would do what had to be done.

Stan left her and she made her own way across the floor, seeing people she hadn't spoken to in years.

"Come over here, Perris," Melody cried at one point. "Kathy and I have the best idea for a winter ski trip to Aspen. What do you think? Just the three of us, or should we bring our husbands?"

"Oh, she'll still be in her honeymoon mood," someone was saying. "You won't be able to drag her off for a week with the girls."

Perris was smiling at them all when a strange thing began to happen. A hush fell over the room, and as she watched, she read in the eyes of her friends what was happening behind her. All faces were turning toward the entrance, but since she had her back to it, she couldn't turn without becoming obvious.

"I don't believe it," Melody whispered to Kathy. "She promised she wouldn't bring him here."

Perris immediately knew the identity of the couple under discussion. She stood where she was, staring at the wall, while the hush deepened throughout the room. Slowly, she turned and faced the entrance.

Robert seemed to stand so much taller than anyone else. He was wearing a white dinner jacket that set off his tan skin. As her eyes met his across the room, everything else faded into a pastel wash of color around them, and she saw only him.

The thick blond hair she'd sunk her fingers into so many times, the well-formed lips she'd kissed with such abandon, the wide shoulders she'd clung to in the tumult of their lovemaking, all belonging to the man she loved so hopelessly, filled her vision and her mind, and she couldn't look away.

His face was hard, and his eyes were cold as he watched her. She could see his gaze drop to inspect the ring on her finger. Too late, she tried to hide it in the folds of her dress. He saw the movement, and something very like a sneer twisted his mouth.

Then Janey was tugging on his arm, and he turned away, smiling down at the other woman, letting her lead him off to the dance floor. All around, the buzzing began, but Perris hardly heard it. She watched, as though hypnotized, while Robert put his arms around Janey and began to swing her across the floor. She might have gone on watching indefinitely if Kathy hadn't intervened.

"Stop it," she ordered sharply. "You're making yourself look like an idiot. Not to mention what it's going to do to Stan." She took Perris by the arm and began leading her toward the bar, talking loudly, as though they'd been in the midst of a conversation all the time.

Perris appreciated what her friend was doing, but she hardly thought it necessary. Everyone knew now. It was too late to try to stuff the cat back into the bag. And Stan would have to admit it, too.

"Where's Stan?" she asked, looking around for him. It was time they faced the facts.

"I think he took your mother home," Gary replied as he reached around her and filled her glass with some-

thing she couldn't identify. She took a long sip of it,
wishing it were lemonade so that she could use it to
quench the awful thirst she had. But this had some sort
of lemon-lime mix in it and would do just as well.
Downing it, she handed back the glass for a refill.

"Don't get carried away," Gary warned, but he
poured her another.

Carried away. That's what Robert had done to her,
carried her away. Only he hadn't completed the job.
Why had he let her go back again? Yes, she knew all
about being carried away.

"Why not?" she asked Gary with a smile, slipping
onto a bar stool. "Don't they drink alcohol to forget, all
those people who do drink it? Don't they all get giggly
and happy no matter what problems they have to face
in the morning? Why can't I do that?"

Gary shook his head and moved closer to her,
looking around as though he wished he could find
Kathy, who'd disappeared in the crowd. "People drink
for a lot of different reasons, but they never drink just to
make it easier to make fools of themselves," he told her
quietly. "And that's what you're going to do if you keep
this up."

"Ah." She nodded wisely. "Other people have valid
reasons for drinking, but mine aren't good enough. Par
for the course." She drank the mixture down and held
out her glass. "Refill, please."

"No, Perris," Gary objected, shaking his worried
head. "You don't need any more."

Perris was feeling very light, as though she could float
away and watch everyone from the ceiling. She threw
back her head and laughed at Gary. "Nonsense,
Gary," she said in what seemed to her to be an
exceedingly witty manner. "Haven't you heard? You've
got to reach out and grab what you want in life."

Taking her own advice, she plucked up a bottle and poured the contents into her own glass, not really caring what she was serving herself.

"That's enough, Perris." Robert's voice cut through her like a sliver of steel. Gary was frowning, not knowing quite how to handle this, and Perris knew that she mustn't turn to look at Robert. She knew how powerless she was once he had her in the spell of his gaze.

She hesitated, then defiantly raised the glass to her lips. Before the liquid could touch her tongue, he took the glass from her and sent it spinning across the bar.

"You're not drinking any more, Perris," he told her calmly.

She lifted her chin indignantly. "And just why not?"

His strong hands took possession of her shoulders, and he pulled her off the stool. "Because you're dancing right now," he answered easily. "The two don't mix."

9

·ᡐᡐᡐᡐᡐᡐᡐᡐᡐᡐᡐᡐ·

Dancing with Robert. Wasn't that how all this had started? She could close her eyes and remember how his warmth had flooded her, how his breath had stirred her hair as he'd guided her around the floor of the restaurant. And now he planned to subdue her that way again.

"I'm not dancing with you," she informed him airily as he led her by the hand toward the dance floor. "You're much too dangerous."

"Dangerous?" His eyes were still cold, but his smile was bemused. He took her to the center of the dance floor, where they were surrounded by swaying couples, and turned her to face him. "Why do you say I'm dangerous?"

She laughed, shaking her head as he tried to take her in his arms. "You know very well how dangerous you are," she said blithely, looking about at the curious faces turned their way. For some reason, the fact that they were becoming the center of attention didn't bother her at all. "You started this whole thing with a dance at Jocko's. Remember?"

"I remember." He stepped closer and slowly slid his arms around her, and she forgot that she wasn't going to dance with him. "I followed you to Jocko's and asked you to dance," he went on softly, just inches from her ear. "You came to me as though you'd been waiting for that invitation all your life."

And she had. Oh, yes, she had. But it didn't do to dwell on those things, especially when her mind was jumping from one thing to another in no apparent pattern. She abandoned herself to his arms and leaned back into the dance.

"Turn very fast," she urged him now. "Spin us across the floor and maybe we'll take off."

"You really shouldn't drink, Perris," he told her with a smile in his voice. "You get awfully silly."

Silly was better than weepy. "Does that mean you're not going to spin us?"

His arm tightened on her back. "If it's spinning you want, spinning you'll get." He began the quick rotation, whirling her around and around. The crowd parted for them, and she wanted to let her head fly back with the centrifugal force and shout "Wheeee," but just when she was starting to do just that, he stopped.

"We didn't take off," she said, sighing. "I was so sure we would."

Why didn't he tell her to grow up or sober up or something equally cutting? She deserved it. Instead, he was holding her closer. His body was so large that she felt as though she could curl up against his chest and be protected forever. But that was an illusion. She was getting too smart to fall for things like that. Wasn't she?

"I remember that night at Jocko's," he said all at once. "I remember how we danced."

"Danced." She laughed again, feeling light and strangely happy. "You could hardly call that dancing. More like making love standing up."

"Of course," he whispered into her hair as he drew his arms more firmly around her. "What is dancing, after all, but an excuse to hold a woman's body very close in public? I hope the person who invented it got the accolades he deserved."

His hand came up under her hair, and he brought her hand to his chest, just as he had that night that seemed so long ago.

"Isn't this how we did it the first time?" he asked her. "Didn't I hold you so that I could feel your pulse with my lips?"

He softly kissed her temple as he had that night, and she shuddered involuntarily.

"And the beat of your heart sent a tingle through my fingertips," she whispered dazedly, pushing aside the heavy white jacket he was wearing so that she could run her hand along the silky warmth inside.

"And your hips fit against mine so well that I knew we were meant to make love to each other." His hand spread across the end of her spine again, forcing her against him.

She was lost and falling, down, down, through a tunnel into the darkness. She had to stop it.

"Don't," she commanded him suddenly, stiffening. "Don't, please. They can see. Everyone can see."

His voice grated on her nerves. "What can they see, Perris? What are you trying to hide?"

She lifted her face to his, searching his eyes. Why not tell him the truth? "They can see how much I love you," she whispered, not flinching from the strength of his gaze.

He stopped dead and stared down at her. She dropped her eyes, hiding her face against his shoulder.

Why had she said that? He knew it already. What was she trying to prod him into?

"Take the ring off, Perris," he said at last, his voice harsh with anger. "You're giving it back to Stan."

She raised her head and opened her mouth in horror. "No, I can't," she whispered wildly. "Not now."

He grasped her arm and pulled her roughly with him back toward the bar. "Right now," he said decisively.

"No," she responded with conviction. "I won't do that to him."

Robert slowed and looked about him. "How do we get out of this place?" he demanded. "We've got to have a little talk."

Mutely, she led the way. The dance floor opened onto the terrace, which was filled with people, but a side stairway led to a little balcony on the other side of the building where they could be alone.

"Listen," he said, swinging her around to face him in the moonlight. "You've got to give Stan that ring back right now, because you're coming with me. I'm not going to listen to any more of your excuses."

She raised her hand and looked at the sparkle of the huge diamond. "I told Stan I loved you," she said simply. "He wants to marry me anyway."

He snorted. "Then he's a fool."

She raised her dark eyes to his. "And what would I be to go with you when you've told me not to count on anything like love?"

Even in the dark she could see the turmoil brewing in his eyes. He seemed about to speak, but then he stopped himself and pulled her to him instead. His mouth came down on hers with a ferocity that startled her, and he used her moment of weakness to penetrate the vulnerable warmth of her mouth, sliding his tongue sensuously into the dark depths.

It was no time for something like this. If he was trying to prove that the magic still sizzled between them, he didn't need to waste his time. She knew it already. They had to talk, to decide what they were going to do. Perris raised both hands to his chest and tried to push him away, but the harder she pushed, the more insistent his kiss became.

Only seconds passed before she stopped pressing against him and her fingers curled against his chest, then began to work their way beneath the white jacket to find the heat below, kneading the silky shirt, feeling for the rough hair beneath the fabric.

The assault upon her mouth was no longer an intrusion. His lips were moving on hers with moist urgency, and she felt herself responding, curling her tongue around his, reaching hungrily for more of him.

"Perris, darling, I thought I'd go crazy without you all week," he rasped into her cheek, rubbing his face against hers as though he couldn't get enough of the feel of her skin. "Don't try to run out on me again. I'm not going to let you."

His hands plunged through the swirling silk of her skirt, curving around her tight bottom, his fingers digging in as he pressed her into the hardness of his hips. She reached high for him, winding her arms around his neck, standing on tiptoe. Her eyes were closed, and she was spinning, turning round and round in a spiral of need for him. She heard a noise that sounded like a cat's purr coming from her own throat, and slowly she arched against him, as though joining him in some necessary ritual of bonding.

"I've got the boat in the water," he told her hoarsely. "Come with me for her test run."

"What?" She opened her eyes and blinked up at him. She would go with him. She would follow him anywhere. But wasn't there something she had to do first?

His mouth was on hers again, taking short, nibbling kisses, gently catching at her lips with his teeth. "Come on," he whispered. "We'll go right now."

She couldn't catch her breath. Everything was moving too fast. Even the sky seemed to be rotating around her. "I have to . . . I must . . ." What was it she had to do? Something about Stan. The ring! She had to give him back his ring.

"You have to tell Stan it's over. We'll go together."

"No." How could she do something like that to Stan? Suddenly, she was very sober. "I'll go to him alone."

She could see that he was about to protest, and she reached up to put a finger to his lips. "I'll go to him alone," she said firmly.

He hesitated, then nodded his agreement. "All right," he said. "Tell him I'm waiting out here if he wants to do something about it."

She stared at him, aghast. "Are you crazy? Do you really think I'm going to let you fight over me like two dogs fighting over a piece of meat?"

He shook his head. "I'll do whatever I have to do to take you. But I'm not going until I'm sure you're coming with me."

Her smile was bittersweet. "I'm coming with you. I don't really have any other choice. But I don't want you here. I have to talk to Stan alone. I wish you'd go so I could be sure. . . ."

He stared at her, then nodded slowly. "Okay," he said, and let her go so that he could reach into the pocket of his slacks. "Here are my keys. I'll go on ahead. You come after me in my car."

"Where shall I meet you?"

"At the marina. I told you, we'll take the boat for a test run."

Suddenly, she grinned. "It's dark, you idiot. Look around you. This is no time to go for a test run."

He looked surprised. "Why not? She's fully equipped with night lights." He touched her chin lightly with one finger. "Meet me at the marina."

"But how are you going to get there if I have your car?"

"I'll borrow a car from a buddy of mine who works as a pro here. Don't worry about me."

She took one last look at the face she loved so much. "All right. I'll be there as quickly as possible."

She hurried to the doorway, but once more he stopped her. "Perris," he called, his voice warm but threaded with warning, "if you don't show up in an hour, I'll come after you. And I'll knock down anything or anybody I have to in order to get you."

She turned away, her heart beating harder with both the excitement of his intensity and her dread of the scene she was about to play out with Stan.

The sea of people inside stunned her, and the bright lights stung her eyes. She gazed around, disoriented for just a moment; then her gaze fell on Greg, and she made her way to his side.

"Do you know where Stan is?" she asked him discreetly.

He looked around at her, surprised. "Oh, didn't he find you? He's been asking around for you."

"I saw him heading for the bar a few minutes ago," said the tall, slender man Greg was talking to.

Perris threw a grateful smile at the man and hurried to the bar. Stan was there, all right, and Gary and Kathy were standing on either side of him as though to protect him from any harm.

"Well, look who's here," Kathy announced as she spotted Perris approaching. From the tone of her voice and the look in her eye, Perris could see that she was feeling loyal to Stan and more than a little angry at the woman who was treating him so badly.

What could she say? Kathy had every right to be angry. Perris deserved every bit of the woman's wrath.

"I've got to talk to you, Stan," she said, touching him on the shoulder.

He stared at her, his eyes dark and troubled. The two of them shared a moment's suspense; then he smiled sadly.

"We can talk here," he told her with infinite weariness. He glanced at his friends, and Gary and Kathy withdrew a small distance away, but stood guard so that no one else would come into the immediate area.

"Don't look so tragic, sweetheart," he told her softly. "It's been miserable from the start. I could see it wasn't going to work. I just didn't know how to end it. But when I saw you with him tonight . . ." He shrugged.

Stan, her darling lifelong friend. How sad she was to do this to him. "I'm so sorry, Stan."

His grin was crooked. "Don't be. We'll always have something special, you and I. It just won't be quite what I was hoping for."

She slipped the ring from her finger and pressed it into his hand. "You deserve so much better," she told him.

He smiled; then the corners of his mouth turned down, and his brows pulled together. "But so do you, Perris. Don't count on too much from Robert Chase."

She shook her head, but she couldn't speak for a moment as tears clogged her throat. "Don't worry about me," she finally managed. "I'm going, Stan. Good-bye."

He pulled her close for a brotherly kiss, and she turned to run out of the bar area. She'd almost made it to the door when Melody caught up with her.

"Perris Fleming, if you think I'm going to let you get away before the announcement—"

Perris turned to confront her friend. "Melody, I'm sorry to spoil your plans, but there isn't going to be any announcement."

Melody's mouth opened and closed like that of a tropical fish. "You can't do this!" she cried at last. "You'll ruin everything."

Perris shrugged helplessly. "I'm sorry." It sounded pretty lame when Melody was facing disaster, but what else could she do for her?

"But . . . but . . . you and Stan announcing your engagement was the centerpiece of the whole theme! Who will I use now?" She frowned in rapid concentration. "Can you think of anyone we might get to propose real quick?"

Perris smiled. "Why not change the focus a little? Use happy marriages as the centerpiece of the romance theme. You and Greg, and Gary and Kathy, can start the whole thing. Have everyone else join a giant conga line, two by two."

Melody looked skeptical. "I don't know. . . ."

"Think about it," Perris called over her shoulder. "Kathy's in the bar. Ask her to help." She made it out the door with no further delays.

The top was down on Robert's little green sports car, and the wind whipped her hair out of its coil on top of her head as she drove down the hill and across London Bridge, toward the marina.

She pulled into the parking lot and turned off the engine, then sat for a moment watching the rows of boats bobbing gently against their moorings. This was insanity, pure and simple. Never had she so blatantly thrown caution to the winds the way she was planning to do tonight. She felt like a woman turning her back on everything life had meant to her, all for the love of a restless man who might not be there when she woke up in the morning.

But any small stirrings of unease evaporated as she noticed a movement on the dock and made out Robert's tall form coming toward her. She left the car quickly and ran down the ramp to meet him.

He caught her in his arms and held her close to him with her face pressed to his chest. Neither of them said a word, but the emotion they each felt flowed between them, strengthening their bond.

If only there were some way she could forge that bond into something permanent—but she wouldn't think about that. Tonight she vowed to surrender completely to the wild passion that had her in its thrall. This night would stand on its own. It wouldn't need plans and promises.

"Everything's ready," he told her, draping an arm around her shoulder as he led her to the boat.

She noticed that he'd changed into jeans and a jersey shirt. "I should have stopped by the house and changed," she realized. "Why don't I just run back and . . . ?"

But Robert was shaking his head. "And take a chance on being sidetracked? No way. I'll take care of you. I'm sure there's something on the boat you can use."

The sailboat looked very different from the last time she'd seen it. Then it had seemed a piece of wood sculpture, motionless in a workroom. Now, with its tall mast and the little white lights at the stern and bow and the red and green lights on the side, it looked like a live thing, eager to sprint.

"This is the test run?" she asked, turning to look at him.

"Well, I did take her out for a bit this afternoon," he

admitted. "But this is the first official test run. After all, you helped build her. No test run would be complete without you."

She let a tiny smile curl the edges of her mouth. "What are we testing for?"

He frowned, all business once again. "The main thing I'm worried about is a little slackness in the rigging. If it gets worse, it could indicate a lack of rigidity in the hull. In other words, it might mean that the hull is flexing and bending. If that's the case, we're in big trouble."

She nodded, trying to match his serious demeanor. "So I'm to look for slackness in the rigging. Anything else?"

"Slackness in the lee shrouds, too. There's bound to be some slackness when the mast leans leeward when we heel, but if the shrouds get slack enough to flop around, once again, we've got problems."

She put her hand to her brow. "Aye, aye, sir," she said smartly. "Seaman Fleming requests you pipe her aboard."

She slipped off her strappy sandals, and he took her hand to help her climb on. Once she'd run from one end to the other, exclaiming how beautiful everything was, reminding him of what she'd done, places she'd sanded, chrome she'd polished, he went down and rummaged in the cabin, bringing out a rumpled bit of blue cloth.

"Take off your dress," he told her, "and put this on."

She held it up to the light, turning it distastefully in her hands. "What is it?"

He looked almost hurt by her lack of enthusiasm. "An old cutoff sweatshirt of mine. I've worn it for years. It'll do fine for you."

"You've got to be kidding! There's no bottom to this."

He was busy untying the lines and casting off, but he looked back at her, his grin lopsided with anticipation. "Yeah. You're going to look great in it."

A nasty suspicion began to form in her mind. Surely he hadn't set her up for this? "I can't wear this." She laughed as she flapped it in the air. "You must have something else."

"Nope." He was busy edging them out of the harbor, and he didn't have time to look her way. "Why don't you just wear your bra and panties, then? It's hot enough for it."

He was right. A sweltering summer wind was blowing through the basin. The temperature hadn't dropped much from the 105 degrees Fahrenheit it had been all day. She really didn't need more than a bra and panties; after all, they were the equivalent of a bikini. The only trouble was, she wasn't wearing a bra.

She looked down at the silk dress, swirling about her now in the wind, then looked at the sweatshirt in her hand. With a shrug, she reached under her skirt and began peeling off her hose.

Her nimble fingers easily found the zipper at the back of the dress, and she pulled it open, catching the light fabric before it fell to the ground and holding it to her chest.

"Do you have something I can put this in to protect it?" she called to him.

He nodded. "There are clothes bags in the cabin."

She went below and found the bags he was talking about. "Why didn't you fill the clothes bags with clothes, Robert Chase?" she grumbled to herself as she folded the dress and zipped it into the protective covering. The cabin was small, just as Robert had predicted when building the boat, but there was room enough for one person to maneuver comfortably. She looked around at the polished wood of the interior and felt a pleasant glow at the beauty of it. Then she glanced down at the sweatshirt in her hand and grimaced.

But she didn't have much choice unless she wanted to go back up on deck as she was, dressed only in her lacy black panties. She slipped the shirt over her head and pulled it down. The ragged hem barely grazed the bottom of her rib cage.

"Robert, my dear," she said to herself through gritted teeth as she gazed at the spectacle she made in the narrow mirror on the little closet door, "I can't let this go unrewarded." Her long legs looked white against the tiny strip of black lace that could hardly be called modest. The arms of the shirt had been cut off above the elbows, and the neck was stretched out of shape.

"I look like a reject from some third-rate Las Vegas chorus line," she muttered as she climbed back up to the deck.

"Nice," Robert said approvingly, his eyes skimming her mostly naked skin and centering on her flat navel.

"Nice?" she murmured, forcing a smile. "I'll show you nice."

She slipped in behind him where he was standing in the cockpit, his hands on the wheel. His attention was riveted on the sail and the weather conditions. The wind was stiff out on the lake, and she knew that he wanted to test the capacity of his boat to respond to every gust.

You just concentrate, Robert, she told him silently. Just see if you can.

The world around them looked like a black velvet wasteland. The lights of the boat sent pools of silver darting over the inky water, reinforcing the feeling of lonely isolation. The warm wind was gusting at the little craft, and Robert was working hard, reaching to ease the sheet one moment, adjusting the sail's camber at another.

"Having trouble?" she asked, both hands on his shoulders, softly working his muscles. She leaned forward, her body touching his back lightly.

"No, she handles like a dream," he called back. "But it'll take time to get used to her idiosyncrasies, to learn how to play her. Especially driving upwind like this. I'm trying to sail as close to the wind as I can."

Robert, Robert, she thought dreamily. So serious. And always so close to the wind. She massaged his shoulders harder, then began to work her way down his back, finding each muscle and kneading it energetically. He moved beneath her hands, and she knew that he liked what she was doing, but he had no time to turn and comment.

"Are we finding any slackness in all those things where we were supposed to watch for it?" she asked at last.

He shook his head. "No. So far, so good."

He turned away suddenly as they came about, tacking at an angle. The sails luffed for a moment, and Robert slacked the jib until they were on the new tack; then he trimmed it hard, slightly slacking the main at the same time. Soon the sails were full again, and they were bearing to windward as before.

Perris leaned toward him and ran her fingers through his thick hair, then reached down and tugged his shirt out of the waistband of his jeans.

"What are you up to, vixen?" he asked over his shoulder.

"You just do your job," she soothed him. "I'll take care of mine."

Hugging herself tightly against his back, she reached around and undid his buttons one by one, running her fingers inside to tangle with the curling hair of his chest. Her hands ran down the center of his chest, down to smooth the hard sides of his belly, to caress the small concave area around his navel, teasing the hair, then back up. She felt him move at her touch, his muscles swelling to fill her hands, and she laughed against the smooth skin of his back.

His shirt flapped in the wind, but she ignored it as she began to work on his back again. She scored the dark skin playfully with her fingernails, drawing patterns that made him writhe, running her hands lightly along his sensitive sides until she'd burrowed her hands into the warm hollows beneath his arms.

"Ah." He let out a long sigh, leaning back toward her. "You're making it very difficult to concentrate."

"Is that so?" she mocked him. "Imagine that."

His jeans were riding low on his hips, and she ran a finger under the belt, experimentally touching the covered skin. Then her arms were around him again, but this time she moved swiftly to unbuckle his belt.

A sudden gust from an unexpected angle hit them at the same moment, and the boat began to heel drastically. Robert reached out for the sheet to slack the mainsail a bit and bring her back to her feet. His mind was on the procedure, and Perris was able to unfasten his belt, release the snap on his jeans and slide the zipper halfway down before he realized what she was doing.

"Perris, what the . . . ?"

Her hands moved beneath his pants, sliding down the scorching heat of his belly to the satin skin of his thighs. She felt him shudder as she moved her fingers across the tiny stiff hairs of his legs, brushing them up with circular movements.

"Oh, Perris . . ." With one angry thrust, he set the wheel and turned to her, pulling her roughly into his strong embrace. "What are you trying to do to me?" His body against hers was like fire meeting fire, and she had to force herself not to respond with the easy abandon that lay so close to the surface.

Instead, she pulled back her head so she could look him in the eye. "Dress me like a tramp and I've got to act the part," she told him coyly.

His gaze swept over her; then a burst of laughter sprang from his throat. "What a delightful prospect," he told her, reaching to flip up the hem of her shirt, exposing one dark nipple and touching it softly with his thumb. "I'll be looking forward to it." His lips descended on her mouth with a kiss that sent her senses spinning once again. "Just hold it at bay for a while. Once we get to Chase Haven, I'll make you keep that promise." He kissed her again. "Now let me sail, mermaid. I don't want to lose my boat on her first night out."

He turned back to the helm, fastening his pants as he did so, but he let his shirt fly out from his back like a white flag of surrender, and she smiled as she watched him.

Throwing her head back, she leaned on the rail and watched the capricious wind fill the sail and carry them like magic through the blackness of the night. When the lights finally began to show them desert sand and palm trees, she knew that they'd found their cove.

"Are you going to tie up to the float again?" she asked as they slowed, sails flapping loosely against the mast.

"No. I'm a little leery of the depth there. We'll drop anchor."

The water was silvery with their light, and the beach looked luminously white in the darkness. Behind the strip of sand, the dark mountains loomed like sand castles pinched from the volcanic earth by a giant hand.

She watched as he threw the anchor overboard and let out the line slowly, until the drag on the bottom brought them to a complete stop. He tossed her a sideways smile, then began to lower the sails.

"Just give me a few minutes, mermaid, and I'll pay you back for that bawdy trick you played on me," he warned.

She looked in toward the shore. Excitement was still singing in her blood, and she felt a wild compulsion to let it take her with it.

"Just what do you plan to teach me?" she asked saucily.

"Oh, I don't know," he answered lazily, lashing the sail to the boom. "I think I'll have to let you do it again, now that I'm able to devote the attention to it that you deserve. Then I'll be better able to decide your punishment."

"Sounds fair," she answered, swinging up onto the side of the boat. "But you'll have to catch me first."

She dove into the dark water, then surfaced and looked back at him as he leaned out over her. "See you in the funny papers," she called back, cocky in the knowledge that he couldn't leave the boat until he'd finished securing the sails.

"You'd better save your energy, Perris," he called back. "When I catch you, you're going to need it."

"Braggart," she teased. "We'll see about that."

She began a long, measured crawl stroke toward the shore. There was no real need to hurry. Robert would be ages yet at his task.

The water was slippery and cool. Though she knew that the surface temperature was a good 80 degrees, that hardly compared to the heat the wind was pouring into the basin.

She was almost to the shore when she heard the sound of a swimmer behind her. She found the rough sand with her feet and looked back. Robert was gaining fast.

Her heart thumped in exhilaration as she ran up through the shallow water, sending silver drops spraying from each running footstep. She heard him lumbering out behind her, but she didn't dare take the time to look back.

The crisp sand crunched beneath her bare feet, and her soggy shirt flapped against her wet skin. She ran up the beach, searching in the gray-blue moonlight for a hiding place but knowing all the time that she'd never find one before he caught her.

She heard him coming up behind her. Laughing, she began to run a zigzag course to avoid capture.

"You run pretty well for a mermaid," he said, chuckling, and she felt herself being pulled back toward him as his hand closed over her wet shirt. "But not quite well enough."

"Oh, no?" She raised her arms and slipped from the shirt, racing off again before he had time to readjust. When she didn't hear him, she turned and found him still standing where she'd left him, holding the sodden cloth in his hand and gazing at the picture she made running across the moonlit sand in nothing but the briefest of black lace panties. He was dressed only in his white briefs himself, having removed his jeans and shirt to swim after her.

"Give up?" she called back, hands on her hips. She knew that when she thought of this night in the future, her cheeks would flame at the memory of the shameless way she was behaving. But for now she was enjoying it. She wanted him to look at her nakedness, wanted to see his response, wanted to feel his arousal.

"Never." He threw the wet shirt onto the sand and began to walk toward her slowly. She'd meant to run again, but something in the set of his shoulders held her where she stood, and she watched him coming to her, unable to move.

"Why aren't you running, mermaid?" he asked softly as he reached her. He stood before her, his blond hair darkened by the water, his shoulders wide as the horizon. "Why aren't you dashing off across the sand?"

"I can't run anymore," she answered breathlessly, staring up into the dark hollows of his eyes. "I'm too afraid you won't catch me."

His grin was a slash of white across his dark face. "I'll catch you, Perris," he told her huskily. "I'll never let you out of my sight."

With one quick movement, he swept her up into his arms, one arm around her shoulders, the other under her knees, and began to carry her off across the long stretch of beach. She snuggled in against him, reaching up to kiss his cool neck.

10

The hot wind caught at her damp hair as he carried her, fanning it out against his shoulder. She began to drop a row of moist kisses just under his jaw line, then ran her tongue across the tiny stubble of his beard.

"Just a little farther," he told her, leaning down to curl his own tongue around her nipple and pull it up into a taut, brown sentinel on her snowy breast. "I have a special place I want to take you to."

He could take her wherever he wished. She knew that she would follow him anywhere. Hungrily, she went on caressing the smooth skin of his neck with her tongue, working slowly up to find the curl of his ear. The taste of him, the full male fragrance, was irresistible, and she went on and on, as though seeking the source of his power over her.

"Perris, darling," he groaned. "You'll have me taking you here on the rocks if you're not careful."

She laughed deep in her throat and gently took his

earlobe between her teeth, tugging provocatively. "I'm
ready when you are," she whispered.

Finally, he stopped and went down on one knee to
place her gently on the ground. The sand was fine and
as soft as warm down. The heat it had absorbed from
the daytime sun was still radiating from it, and Perris felt
as though she were resting on a cloud. She leaned back
and looked about her at the overhanging rocks, the
black-eyed Susans growing in clumps around her, the
blue-black sky above.

"Lie still, mermaid," Robert murmured, still on his
knees while he looked down at her on the sand. "It's
time I paid you back for what you did to me on the
boat."

She smiled up at him, her eyes glittering from
beneath her long lashes as she narrowed her eyes. "Be
fair, now," she urged. "Make sure the punishment fits
the crime."

"Oh, it will fit, all right." His hands began a slow
exploration of her body, starting with the sunken circle
about her navel and working out to encompass her
jutting hip bones, her rounded hips. "Your misdeeds
will receive their just rewards."

His fingertips set off tiny tremors as they rubbed
teasingly across the length of her thighs, coming again
and again to the sensitive inner flesh. She began to
move convulsively, reaching to pull him in for more
intimate contact, but he evaded her.

"Oh, no, my little imprisoned mermaid," he rasped.
"The prisoner doesn't dictate the penalty."

Gently, he forced her flat on her back once more, his
night-darkened eyes burning into hers. "Lie still," he
said again. "Lie still and take your punishment like the
siren that you are."

She threw back her head and stared at the stars while
his fingers climbed her ribs as though they were a

stairway, ending at the circles of her breasts. His hands were so large that they could encircle the two soft shapes, thumbs touching at the bottom, and slowly he massaged them, working steadily toward the tight tips.

But just before he touched them, he stopped, looking down at her, waiting, and she began to writhe, moving to force his hands to cover her completely and bring some measure of fulfillment to the longing he was igniting inside her.

"Tell me what you want, mermaid," he prodded softly. "Let me hear you say it."

"You," she said hoarsely, her eyes blurred with desire. "I want you so badly. Oh, Robert, come here!"

"Not yet." His laugh was low and amused. She could see that he was enjoying his special brand of torture. But why not? Hadn't she enjoyed doing the same to him? "You still have to pay your forfeit."

He leaned down and teased each nipple in turn with his warm tongue, holding each breast with both hands as he did so. She twisted and moaned beneath the electricity of his touch, stabbing her fingers into his thick hair, trying to force his head down harder, but he showed no mercy.

"Gently, darling. Take it easy. We've got all night."

He raised his head and looked at her. "My sweet mermaid, pulled from the water," he murmured, his mouth closing on hers in tender adoration. She squirmed, trying to edge her body closer to his, while his kiss took away what breath she had left.

Slowly, his hands slipped down again, until his fingers skimmed the elastic of the black lace at her hips. She groaned as he hesitated, turning and lifting to meet his hand, crying out in satisfaction as it finally plunged beneath the lace to find the heart of her warmth.

He lowered himself beside her, and she turned wildly

to pull him closer, running her hands over his skin, reveling in the tingling it set off against the surfaces of her palms.

"You know what happens this time, don't you, little mermaid?" he asked her roughly, his breathing as uneven as her own. "This time, making love to the human will change you into a human yourself. There will be no more security of the ocean to run to. You'll have to stay out and brave the world without it."

A fire burned within her more fiercely than any had ever burned before. Her mind, her touch, every sense she possessed, were wrapped up in a passion so intense that it seemed to throb more loudly than her heart itself. She hardly heard his words, but she could tell from the tenor of his voice that he was saying something he considered significant, so she frowned, trying hard to understand.

"Do you get it, Perris?" he said more harshly. "I'm not going to let you go again. This time you're making a commitment. If you make love with me now, you're going with me when I leave Lake Havasu."

Of course she would go with him. How could she ever have thought that anything else would be possible? She nodded, sliding her hands down to begin peeling away his briefs.

His hard hand stopped her. "Do you understand?" he demanded.

"Yes," she whispered throatily. "Anything. Only love me, Robert. I can't stand it anymore."

He came to her then, and they joined in a raging rhythm as elemental as the pounding of their blood, as old as man himself, yet as new as they would make it every time.

She cried out as they neared the ultimate, and in her frenzy felt her teeth press slightly into his shoulder, but the sensual pressure only drove him higher, and his fingers dug into her bottom as the crest was attained, pulling her to him in delicious agony.

"Perris," he gasped, not letting her go even when the thrill began to fade away, "remember your promise. Don't try to back out."

Her eyes were closed, and she reached out to wrap her arms around his neck, holding him close. What was it that she'd promised? She couldn't quite remember. Not yet. She'd think about that later. Right now, all she wanted was to float on the golden cloud where Robert had joined her. "I love you, Robert," she whispered, almost more to herself than to him. "I love you; I love you."

That seemed to satisfy him, and he lapsed into silence with her. They listened to the lapping of the small waves along the lake shore. It seemed to be the only sound in the night other than their breathing, although Perris knew that this side of the lake abounded with deer, wild burros, coyotes and cougars.

Her eyes shot open as she thought of that. She began to listen more carefully. Was that a rustling she heard in the chaparral? Surely that was a burro snorting.

"What's the matter?" Robert drew himself up to look at her. "Why did you go so tense all of a sudden?"

"Animals," she whispered, pushing him aside so that she could sit up beside him. "Wild animals. Didn't you hear something?" Her eyes were wide as she looked about in the darkness, but they turned on Robert when he laughed at her.

"Don't be silly," he told her. "There's nothing here that will hurt you."

His arms curled around her shoulders, and suddenly she knew he was right. Nothing would hurt her as long as he was there.

"Look at the lights across the lake," she said.

"They're so bright. Can you see which ones belong to the country club?"

His arm tightened around her. "The country club doesn't matter anymore," he reminded her gruffly. "Very soon we'll be leaving, you and I."

She held back a sigh. She knew what she'd promised, and she meant to keep that promise. What else could she do? She loved Robert. She couldn't stay there without him. Yes, when the time came, she would go with him. She would stay with him, too, for however long he wanted her.

But her mother, her poor mother. To have to grasp her own happiness out of her mother's despair was a bitter thing.

"How long will we be gone?" she asked quietly.

He moved restlessly beside her. It was almost as though he could read her mind and knew her reservations.

"However long it takes," he said.

"Are you planning to try to take the boat around the world?" She hoped he wasn't. Not that the thought of such an adventure didn't stir her now. And come to think of it, it did, she realized with surprise. But that wasn't the problem. It was leaving her mother that bothered her.

She had no more doubts about Robert. He might not believe in love, but he wanted her for now. And she would take what she could get. She would let his summer wind fill her sails and carry her off.

"I've about given that up," he told her. "For now, anyway. But there is a race around the world planned for next summer. I'm thinking about that one."

Perhaps he expected their affair to be over by then. She looked out at the little boat lying gracefully at anchor in the bay. "How are you going to get her out to the ocean?" she asked.

"The usual way," he replied. "I have a trailer. We'll rent a bigger car and tow her out."

Suddenly, he swung her around in his arms. "You're coming with me?" he asked, and she was startled to see the vulnerability in his eyes. "You're really coming with me?"

She nodded, a smile breaking through. "Yes, Robert," she said simply. "I'm really coming with you."

His grin was wide and exultant as he pulled her close to his chest. "Thank God" was all he said. He held her there for a long time, then put a finger under her chin to tilt her face up for his kiss.

"There's only one thing I worry about," she began, then stopped when she saw the rush of hardness in his face.

"What's that?" he asked with soft expectancy.

She hesitated. "My mother. I hate to leave her alone. I don't know what she'll do without me, especially now that I've ruined another one of her dreams."

He drew away from her. "Your mother will do just fine," he said firmly.

She shook her head. "No, you don't know her."

His laugh was short. "That's where you're wrong. I know her very well."

"What are you talking about?" He must mean something else. His relations with his family had never been close. Perhaps he was going to tell her how unrealistic she was being. Perhaps he was going to explain how unimportant mothers were.

"I know your mother," he replied. "Didn't she ever tell you the name of her woodworking instructor at the community center?"

Perris stared at him. "No," she whispered, stunned. "She never told me."

He shrugged. "I've been volunteering at the center since I moved here. I go over there every afternoon."

Still she stared. "I don't believe it."

He reached over and ruffled her drying hair. "Believe it, Perris. Your mother has a real touch for woodworking. She started out just watching, but she really gets into it now."

"But she promised me she wouldn't do anything strenuous."

His sigh showed what he thought of that. "Listen, Perris. Unused muscles atrophy. You know that. The mind, the body, everything, has to be used to face new challenges. Otherwise, they wither on the vine. If you protect your mother too much, she'll lose the ability to protect herself."

She knew that there was something in what he was saying, but still, this was her mother. She'd been through a lot. He just didn't understand.

"She's so weak . . ." she began, but he laughed before she could finish.

"Weak? You should see that little lady with a chisel in her hand, attacking a block of cherry wood."

Perris turned away, frowning. She wasn't sure that Robert saw her mother as she really was. How could he be expected to? But at least they knew one another. What did her mother think of Robert?

"Are the two of you . . . friends?" she asked.

He nodded. "We're great pals. I like her, and I think she likes me." He reached out to take the fullness of her naked breast gently in his hand. "It's getting late," he noted. "Time we got back." He took her fully in his arms and rocked her. "I'm going to take you home and clean you up, little mermaid. And keep you forever."

Forever. That had a nice ring to it. But she mustn't take things like that seriously. Everyone said them. They meant nothing. So she laughed. "Where, as a trophy on your wall?"

"No." He kissed her cheek. "As a woman in my

bed . . . and my life," he amended quickly as her eyes opened wide with indignation.

"That's right," she said smugly. "Remember, I'm not a mermaid anymore."

"No, you're not." He rose, pulling her with him. "But you're going to have to swim like one to get back to the boat."

"Don't worry. I haven't lost all my mermaid talents," she reassured him. They strolled along the beach, picking up her shirt and other discarded garments. Then they both plunged into the water and swam lazily back toward the well-lit boat.

Once on board, Robert found a blanket to drape around Perris. Then he climbed back into his jeans, and they got underway again, running with the wind this time, sailing toward their future.

"Have you named your boat yet?" Perris asked at one point. "I don't remember seeing anything on the transom."

"Not yet," he said shortly. Then he grinned. "How about *The Sexy Mermaid*? Then you could ride out there on the bow like a figurehead on one of the old sailing ships."

"Oh, sure. Topless and dressed in a fishtail, I suppose?"

He shrugged carelessly. "Why not? Sounds good to me."

She threw him a dagger-sharp look. "I'm not a mermaid anymore, remember?"

He shook his head. "That's right. Such a shame. But we mustn't forget your roots no matter how human you become."

She made a face at him, and they both laughed. It was warm and good having this companionable feeling between them again. Perris felt a deep sense of wonder that it could be so fulfilling.

She watched the lights of the city getting closer, and she almost dreaded their return. What time was it now? Was everyone asleep?

"You know, you just left Janey at that party," she exclaimed suddenly as the thought came to her.

He grinned. "Don't worry about that lady. I'm sure she found a ride home."

"But did you ever tell her . . . ?"

"She knew from the beginning what I was there for. I asked her to get me in so that I could see you. She didn't expect me to take her home."

"Oh." So he'd planned to kidnap her from the first. She smiled secretly, enjoying that fact. "You did miss me, then."

"Miss you?" His voice was gruff, but his eyes were on the sail. "I couldn't breathe without you. I couldn't eat; I couldn't sleep. I knew I had to get you back for my own survival."

She laughed. "I felt pretty much the same way," she admitted. Maybe Robert didn't believe in love, but he certainly exhibited all the symptoms. Was there any way she could teach him how to recognize the cause and nurture it rather than trying to deny its existence?

They docked and made the boat fast, then spent a good deal of time preparing to leave it. Perris helped all she could while holding the blanket around her with one hand. When they finally left the marina in Robert's little car, the purple-pink light of morning was creeping over the tops of the mountains.

He drove them straight to the Castlemeyer house, and they went in through the garage.

"Shall we take a bath in your room?" Perris asked, starting up the stairs, but to her surprise, Robert hesitated.

"I don't know," he said slowly. "Mrs. Castlemeyer's back and . . ."

"What?" Perris whirled, snapping at him. "You brought me back here like this when Mrs. Castlemeyer's here?"

"Did you think I'd be shocked?" The voice came from up the stairs, and Perris turned. The lady was small and white-haired, but there was a glow of vitality in her snapping black eyes that endeared her to Perris at once. She wore a bright peach-colored dressing gown, and she came bouncing down the stairs as though it were noon rather than the wee hours of the morning.

"I've lived too long, my dear, and in too many weird places for much to shock me anymore." She smiled. "Perris Fleming, isn't it? Robert has told me all about you. Come along. I think the British Isles is your best place today."

Perris followed meekly, throwing one last beseeching look down at Robert, who was grinning back. He gave her a jaunty wave and started for his own room, but she had no time to say good-bye, because Mrs. Castlemeyer was still talking.

She talked while she filled the old-fashioned claw-footed tub full of hot, sudsy water; she talked while she stripped the moth-eaten blanket from around Perris; she talked while Perris luxuriated in the warm water, closing her eyes and letting the words run over her like a spring shower.

"I love your house," Perris roused herself enough to say at one point. "I hope you don't mind that Robert showed me all your special rooms."

"Mind? Why should I mind? I love to show them off. Some friends have recommended that I turn the place into a museum, and I might just do that someday. After all, I have no descendants to leave it to, and I don't think Robert wants it."

"Robert?" Perris rose in the water and looked at the

old woman in surprise. "I thought Robert was your caretaker."

The little woman laughed heartily. "What ever gave you that idea? Oh, no, my dear. Robert is an old friend of mine. He saved my husband's estate when Farley died. Farley was a great Foreign Service officer, but after retirement he tried his hand at corporate politics and was a real flop. He made a lot of money, but when he died, the scum he worked with tried to keep it all for themselves. I asked around for the best corporate lawyer in San Francisco, and I found Robert. He took over, saved everything my husband left me and got a nice settlement for my trouble, as well. He became the best friend I ever had."

She laughed again. "You know Robert. He throws himself heart and soul into everything he does. No other attorney could have done what he did for me or taken such a personal interest. So when he said he wanted to take a few years off, build a boat and sail around the world, I offered him this house to do his building in. I knew he would get the peace and quiet he needed after that rat race in the city."

Perris was still trying to digest this news. "Do you mean to tell me that Robert is an attorney at law?" Her voice sounded squeaky.

"You thought he was just a caretaker, did you?" Mrs. Castlemeyer shook her head. "I must say, your lack of perception disappoints me, dear. I had hoped you had a mind in that pretty head. Robert will need a woman with some sense, since he has very little of that himself. He's a darn good lawyer, but he worked so hard at it that he got burned out, needed some time off."

Perris let the old lady babble on without listening. Her blood was boiling with anger. He'd known what she thought, and he'd been laughing at her all the time!

She dressed in the British room, not even seeing the lovely decorations. Mrs. Castlemeyer lent her an apricot silk dressing gown that flowed around her ankles. She used a blow dryer to fix her hair. Then she thanked her hostess and ran out to look for Robert.

She caught him coming in from the kitchen.

"Robert Chase," she announced angrily, "I want a word with you."

Despite her anger, her heart lurched at the picture he made, so fresh and clean in his dark blue slacks and crisp white shirt. His blond hair gleamed in the morning sunlight that was streaming in through the skylight above him. She loved him so. Why had he played with her this way?

His grin was sheepish. "Oh-oh. What's Mrs. Castlemeyer been telling you?"

She came to a stop before him, her hands on her hips. "Why didn't you tell me you were a professional man? What was all this garbage about your poverty-stricken childhood?"

He smiled ruefully. "The poor background was no lie, Perris. I told you exactly what it was like. I guess I neglected to fill in some of the later details."

"You said you never finished high school!"

He shrugged. "I never really did. I took an equivalency test and went on from there, working my way through college and law school."

"You left out all of those details." She spread her palms in bewilderment. "Why did you do that?"

He took her by the shoulders tenderly. "It started out as kind of a gag. Then I wanted to teach you something. I was hoping to make you learn to take risks. I wanted you to let yourself fall in love with me even though it didn't seem like such a safe thing to do."

"Robert!"

"Hush." He put a finger to her lips. "We'll finish this discussion later. Your mother is waiting to see you."

She looked at him blankly. "My mother?"

He nodded. "I invited her over for breakfast."

Perris groaned in horror. "Oh, no. What will she think, finding me here like this?"

He took her in his arms, his hand sliding into the opening of her dressing gown and cupping one full breast. "She'll think we've had a night of torrid love. And she'll be absolutely right."

"But . . ." Perris groped for something to say, but words eluded her.

"Let's join her, shall we?" He dropped a quick kiss on her parted lips, then led her into the breakfast nook, where her mother was seated at the little breakfast table, heartily eating a plateful of scrambled eggs, bacon and blueberry muffins.

"Mother." Perris leaned down to give her a hug. "Oh, Mother, I'm so sorry. Do you know about Stan?"

Her mother was dressed in a violet suit and looked unusually chipper. She nodded. "I saw Robert come in last night, and I knew it was all over. I asked Stan to drive me home so as to get him out of the way for a while. Poor boy, he was rather glum. But we had a nice talk. He knew it was for the best."

Perris sank into a chair beside her mother. "I'm so sorry," she said again. "I know how much you wanted Stan and me to . . ."

"Perris," her mother broke in, "that's not really true. What I wanted for you was happiness, the sort of happiness a great love can bring. I had that with your father. I was hoping you would have it, too. I love Stan as a son, but I certainly would never foist him on you just for my own sake!"

"Oh, Mother." Perris hugged her again.

"I understand, all right." Her mother chuckled. "I saw you and Robert looking at one another across that crowded floor, and I understood immediately."

"Then you don't mind if we . . . ?"

"You two belong together; that much is clear." She lifted her coffee cup to her lips and took a long sip. "You have my unqualified blessings."

But did she understand everything? Perris bit her lip, knowing that she had to explain fully. "You do know that we'll be gone for a while."

Her mother nodded. "Sailing all over the Pacific in that silly little boat. Yes, Robert has told me all about it. I can't say it's something I would want to do, but I hope you both have a wonderful time."

"And you'll be all right alone?" The guilt was still with her. She supposed it always would be.

"Of course." Her mother looked indignant. "Perris, darling, I'm an adult woman. I can take care of myself. It's true I've had a bad setback this year, but I'm coming out of it."

"She certainly is," Mrs. Castlemeyer agreed, sailing in to put a vase of fresh flowers on the table. "And I'm going to make it my personal business to keep her on a constant treadmill." She dashed out again, an empty vase in her hands.

"You see?" Mrs. Fleming smiled at her daughter. "I'm going to be just fine."

Perris was happy, but all this was happening too fast. She knew that her mother still didn't comprehend the difference between marriage with Stan and what she would have with Robert. She had to try to make it clear now, or there would be major recriminations in the future.

"You do understand that the relationship Robert and I will have . . . won't include a house with a garden around it, don't you?" she asked tentatively.

Robert had been standing in the background, letting the two of them talk, but now he moved forward and leaned both hands on Perris's shoulders from behind. "Not at first, anyway," he agreed. "But I'll tell you what. Why don't we promise your mother to have a super house plus a garden by the time our first child is born?"

Perris swung around and stared up into his laughing eyes. "Our first child?" she echoed dully.

He nodded. "Children are often one of the fruits of a successful marriage, aren't they?"

Her jaw dropped even farther. "Marriage?" she repeated.

He cocked an eyebrow toward her mother. "A little slow this morning, isn't she? I suppose all that midnight swimming does affect the brain. Or at least the hearing."

Her mother nodded. "Mornings never were her best time," she told him conspiratorially. "Perhaps if you put it in writing and brought it in along with her orange juice and the morning paper . . . ?"

"I can't wait that long." He looked back down at Perris. "But it might help if I took her out and proposed to her. What do you think?"

"I think that would be an excellent idea," Mrs. Fleming agreed. "And it will give me time to finish this lovely blueberry muffin."

Perris followed Robert out into the green belt, her mind whirling. She knew what she'd heard, but somehow the pieces weren't falling into logical order for her. She was afraid to let herself believe it all.

Robert led her through the orange trees to the gazebo. On the steps, he knelt on one knee before her and took her hand. "Perris Fleming," he said soberly, "will you please, please marry me?"

She gazed down at him, her brow creased in bewil-

derment. "Robert, I just don't know," she said hesitant-
ly. "I thought you didn't believe in love."

He laughed softly as he came to his feet and took her
in his arms. "One of my many character flaws," he told
her softly, his lips near her ear. "I don't believe in
anything until I see the proof for myself." His breath
was feathering her cheek, sending tiny tremors across
her skin. "But you proved it to me, darling. You taught
me that love is real and growing stronger all the time."

"But you said I shouldn't count on love from you, not
the sort of love—"

"Perris, I could cut out my tongue for saying those
words. I knew, deep down, that I loved you in exactly
that way, but I was afraid to admit it. Once I'd had the
scare of seeing you really engaged to Stan, I knew what
a fool I'd been."

Still she shook her head, uncertain. "What about
letting the wind fill your sails?" she reminded him.
"What about freedom?"

"Perris, Perris, I've never felt freer in my life than I do
in your arms." He held her more tightly, pressing every
curve and angle against his hardness. "Will you marry
me?"

His mouth found hers, and his tongue echoed the
persuasion of his words. When he finally drew back, she
was panting at the strength of his argument.

"One more bit of evidence in this case," he told her
softly, holding her gently to him. "I've decided on a
name for the boat. I'm going to have it painted on
today."

"What is it?" she asked, closing her eyes to revel in
the feel of his masculinity all around her. The smell of
the orange blossoms combined with his fresh male
scent to make her dizzy. It was true, and she was finally
starting to admit it to herself. He did love her. They
were going to be together forever, just as she'd never

dared to hope. The joy that thought brought to her surged through her body, filling her with a radiant happiness like nothing she'd ever felt before.

"I'm going to call her *I Love Perris*," he announced.

She looked up into his blue eyes. "As in the song?" she asked. "'In the springtime'?"

"No," he growled, coming in to nip the sensitive skin of her neck. "As in the emotion. I love Perris. I love her now; I love her for always and forever."

"Oh," she said, smiling into his blond hair. "In that case, I guess I will marry you." She reached up to slip her arms around him. "But I think we should name her *Summer Wind*."

"*Summer Wind*? Why?"

She smiled up at him, reaching to push his blond hair back from his forehead. "Because that's how I think of you—as a hot summer wind that came racing down from the canyons and stirred the embers of my life into flame."

He chuckled softly, pulling her back against his chest. "How about *I Love Perris in the Summer Wind*?"

"We'll have to build a bigger boat to fit that title."

He kissed the top of her head. "We have all the time in the world to decide on a name," he said softly.

She hugged him tightly. "And the freedom," she murmured.

"And the freedom," he echoed, holding her against his heart.

YOU'LL BE SWEPT AWAY WITH SILHOUETTE DESIRE

$1.75 each

1 ☐ James
2 ☐ Monet
3 ☐ Clay
4 ☐ Carey

5 ☐ Baker
6 ☐ Mallory
7 ☐ St. Claire

8 ☐ Dee
9 ☐ Simms
10 ☐ Smith

$1.95 each

11 ☐ James
12 ☐ Palmer
13 ☐ Wallace
14 ☐ Valley
15 ☐ Vernon
16 ☐ Major
17 ☐ Simms
18 ☐ Ross
19 ☐ James
20 ☐ Allison
21 ☐ Baker
22 ☐ Durant
23 ☐ Sunshine
24 ☐ Baxter
25 ☐ James
26 ☐ Palmer
27 ☐ Conrad
28 ☐ Lovan

29 ☐ Michelle
30 ☐ Lind
31 ☐ James
32 ☐ Clay
33 ☐ Powers
34 ☐ Milan
35 ☐ Major
36 ☐ Summers
37 ☐ James
38 ☐ Douglass
39 ☐ Monet
40 ☐ Mallory
41 ☐ St. Claire
42 ☐ Stewart
43 ☐ Simms
44 ☐ West
45 ☐ Clay
46 ☐ Chance

47 ☐ Michelle
48 ☐ Powers
49 ☐ James
50 ☐ Palmer
51 ☐ Lind
52 ☐ Morgan
53 ☐ Joyce
54 ☐ Fulford
55 ☐ James
56 ☐ Douglass
57 ☐ Michelle
58 ☐ Mallory
59 ☐ Powers
60 ☐ Dennis
61 ☐ Simms
62 ☐ Monet
63 ☐ Dee
64 ☐ Milan

65 ☐ Allison
66 ☐ Langtry
67 ☐ James
68 ☐ Browning
69 ☐ Carey
70 ☐ Victor
71 ☐ Joyce
72 ☐ Hart
73 ☐ St. Clair
74 ☐ Douglass
75 ☐ McKenna
76 ☐ Michelle
77 ☐ Lowell
78 ☐ Barber
79 ☐ Simms
80 ☐ Palmer
81 ☐ Kennedy
82 ☐ Clay

YOU'LL BE SWEPT AWAY WITH SILHOUETTE DESIRE

$1.95 each

83 ☐ Chance	88 ☐ Trevor	93 ☐ Berk	98 ☐ Joyce
84 ☐ Powers	89 ☐ Ross	94 ☐ Robbins	99 ☐ Major
85 ☐ James	90 ☐ Roszel	95 ☐ Summers	100 ☐ Howard
86 ☐ Malek	91 ☐ Browning	96 ☐ Milan	101 ☐ Morgan
87 ☐ Michelle	92 ☐ Carey	97 ☐ James	102 ☐ Palmer

READERS' COMMENTS ON SILHOUETTE DESIRES

"Thank you for Silhouette Desires. They are the best thing that has happened to the bookshelves in a long time."

—V.W.*, Knoxville, TN

"Silhouette Desires—wonderful, fantastic—the best romance around."

—H.T.*, Margate, N.J.

"As a writer as well as a reader of romantic fiction, I found DESIREs most refreshingly realistic—and definitely as magical as the love captured on their pages."

—C.M.*, Silver Lake, N.Y.

*names available on request